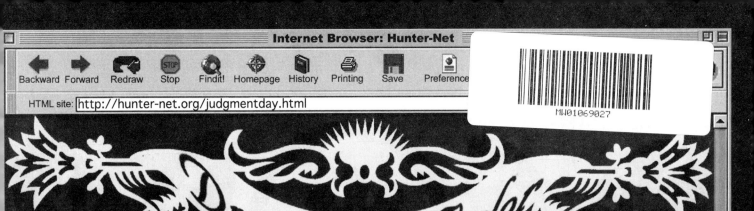

Welcome to the Drumskin Tattoo Parlor web page. Drumskin is a real shop where the human body is our canvas. That doesn't mean we can't branch out onto the electronic canvas, though.

We're always searching for new images and designs to add to our repertoire. In particular, we want cultural and religious icons to offer to our customers, and sometimes we need help doing it. For example, we've discovered the following piece but have yet to identify its source or origins. If you can name or explain it for us, you'll win a temporary-tattoo decal of your choice. Just email us at the address below.

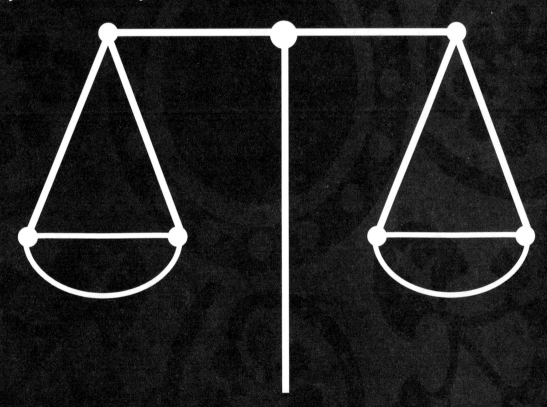

drumskin_tattoos@hotmail.com

Search terms: balance, justice, hunt, rightandwrong, monsters, judgment, message, judgmentday

PROLOGUE: BEST JUDGMENT

July

The club called *Rubies* didn't have a sign or a canopy, but it did have a bouncer. He looked at the trio before him and saw they didn't quite click. The big one kept looking at the other two for reassurance — he'd seen that before — but they didn't seem eager enough, as most guests did. Or maybe theirs just wasn't the right kind of eager. The old man wore a black turtleneck and a long coat, but without style. The woman wore a velvet dress that was too late by a couple of months. She herself was late by years. And the big guy's shirt collar was beginning to fray, which at least made it consistent with his worn-out jacket.

It was past two, the bouncer was tired, and he had a bit of a contact high. But still. He almost waved the three of them in, then decided to give them a hard time.

"What's the password?" the bouncer asked. He smiled as he said it, as if it were a joke.

The old man scowled. His eyes were mirthless and intense.

"I have no time for this," he said coldly. Each word was precisely bitten off. The bouncer narrowed his eyes, now a bit uneasy.

"You're not making me want to let you in," he cautioned, dredging up a weary version of his best tough-guy leer.

The old man pulled up his left coat and shirt sleeves. "I'm expected," he said with contempt.

The bouncer looked at the lines of bandages, brown with old blood. He stepped aside and let them in.

The club was thick with smoke and dense with music that thrummed low and suggestively. Only a few people were drinking at the bar. Someone who watched for a long time might notice that many of the people inside eventually drifted back through a curtain, off to one side of the stage.

The three moved to the bar. The big one got a beer, which he sipped frequently. The old man got a brandy, which he held but never raised to his lips. The woman drank nothing. They waited, squinting into the dark and mostly remaining silent.

They waited until Allison Smalls came from the back room. The old man identified her, of course. It was smoky, dark and late, and they knew her only from class photos and grainy videotape, but he was sure. They watched her and her two friends. Once Allison stumbled out the door, they counted to sixty then followed. The old man had both hands in his coat pockets. The big one had his jacket partially unzipped.

Outside, the bouncer was nowhere to be seen.

The woman went to get their van while two men followed the three youngsters. When the pursuers saw the vehicle round the corner, they exchanged nods and broke into a run, pistols in hand.

"Freeze! Police! Don't move!"

One of Allison's friends bolted. The "cops" didn't care. Allison and the remaining young man raised their hands.

"On the ground! Now! Do it!" The big one did all the shouting. As the bewildered youngsters knelt, the old man reached into his pocket and produced a second weapon, a stun gun.

"Hey… you aren't cops!" Allison's companion yelled. The van pulled up and its side door rattled open.

"Shut your fuckin' mouth," the big man said. It didn't escape the boy's notice that he'd angered the most menacing attacker. The kid wanted to look up at the man's face or try to read the van's license plate, but he couldn't take his eyes off the barrel of the pistol aimed right at his face. To him it looked as big and black and deep as a railway tunnel.

"What are you doing?" Allison demanded as the old man approached her. He had a small semiautomatic in his right hand, the stun gun in his left. He said nothing as he stepped close and jammed the latter weapon's electrodes into her, right at the base of her neck.

"Hurry up," the woman shouted from the van.

"Can you get her?" the old man asked, glancing toward his large companion. The big man nodded, and the old man pointed his gun at the kneeling boy.

"Where are you taking her?" the boy screamed.

"Be quiet," the old man said. "You will not fare well if left here unconscious." His voice was blank as a piece of white paper, and he gestured slightly with the stun gun.

"Come on, Doc," the big man urged. The old man stepped into the van but never shifted his gaze from the boy. Then the door closed and the van sped away.

*　　　　*　　　　*

The woman was Dr. Laura Jenson. The two men were Duane Kinniard and Dr. Carleton Van Wyk. They took Allison far from the city to a rented cabin in a wooded area with few people to be curious about what the three had to do there. On the way, Van Wyk examined the girl and said that she seemed stable, though in expectedly poor health. Duane handcuffed her to himself as a precaution, although doing so proved to be needless. She was still uncon-

scious when he carried her into the cabin and gently placed her on a bed. Then the two doctors put her in a straitjacket.

Later, the two men sat outside on the porch. Duane took long swigs of beer. Van Wyk had water. After the girl came to, they could hear Laura begin to speak, identifying herself as a psychiatrist hired by Allison's parents to care for her. Both men listened, wondering whether the "patient" would scream. She didn't.

"She's taking it well," Van Wyk said.

"Poor kid. At least grabbing her went down smooth enough," Duane said. Van Wyk nodded. Eventually, Duane spoke again.

"I spotted some puppets in the club, I think, but no vampires."

"I imagine they were in the back."

"Think we should go back and clear 'em?"

"Not there. Too public. If Ripsaw wants to take his chances with a SWAT team, that's his business. Eventually, we might trace them back to their residences and make daylight raids. Good sense seems to favor that strategy."

"Yeah. Still, it's kind of frustrating, don't you think? I mean, that we have to let them keep at it, feeding on kids like her."

"She made her choice. She's fortunate her parents can afford to have her 'deprogrammed.' Fortunate that she's still young enough to be easily committed."

They were silent. Again, it was Duane who spoke first.

"I never thought I'd wind up doing this. 'Deprogrammer.' Shit. 'Course, I never expected to be seeing monsters, either."

Van Wyk made no reply. Just as Duane was about to ask him whether he ever worried about Laura, Van Wyk gestured for silence.

"I think there's something out—" was as far as he got before something attacked. It was a blur, streaking from the trees and slashing bright metal across Duane's face and chest. Van Wyk leaped from the porch and struggled to free his gun. In the time it took him to draw, the vampire was upon him. His leather coat took the worst of the thrust, but the assailant's knife still scraped skin from Van Wyk's ribs. The old man saw it raise its knife hand to stab his face, and then Duane jumped onto its back, a knife of his own in hand. To Van Wyk's eyes, Duane's weapon virtually quivered with energy. Duane's free hand went across the creature's face, pulling back its head. His right hand slashed the blade across the creature's throat and cut through flesh, vein and trachea. Blood boiled where the knife had passed.

"Raymond!"

Allison's voice rang, even through the window panes. Duane turned. He saw the girl staring in terror through the glass, then struggling as Laura tried to pull her back. And while he was distracted, their attacker slipped free and charged back into the night.

Van Wyk's attention never wavered. "Halt!" he shouted. His voice was hard with authority, but his command was futile. Despite his exceptional senses, he'd already lost sight of the attacker and was unable to prevent the creature's escape.

*   *   *

August

Laura had picked the restaurant. Van Wyk didn't usually go for such places — ferns, memorabilia and drinks with clever names did nothing for him. But it was Laura's favorite place. She'd said that if the news was good, she'd want to celebrate. Otherwise, she'd want to be consoled.

As she walked in, he could see it would be consolation.

"Hello, Doctor Jenson." He stood, pulled out her chair. His brow was furrowed, and his manners were even more formal than usual.

"I don't know if you'll be able to call me that much longer." Her voice was as brittle as her smile.

"They recommended that your license be revoked?"

She nodded.

"That's ridiculous! I beg you to fight this, it's…." He stopped, took a deep breath. "I'm sorry, where are my manners? Please, let me get you a drink."

"No, I'd… I'll just give it to you straight."

"I appreciate your candor."

She laughed, but the sound was strangely sad. "You talk like a book, Carleton."

He smiled back faintly and no less sadly, not bothering to interpret what she meant. "You flatter me." The smile faded. "What happened in court?"

"Allison testified. She broke down in tears, talking about 'Raymond' and you and Duane…. I didn't give them your names."

Van Wyk let out the breath he had been holding unconsciously. "Thank you. You don't know what that means to me."

"I have some idea." She looked at him for a moment, then continued. "Anyway, it didn't look good that BCAN wouldn't name two of its employees. The cops testified again and again that there was no body, no evidence that any violence had occurred, reiterated that the abduction was legal. It didn't matter. The psychiatrist testifying for their side was very persuasive, and Allison did look…

what's the phrase? 'Crazy as a shithouse rat?' So they found for malpractice."

"Imbeciles."

"It gets better. Or worse, I suppose. Her father has filed a pair of civil suits. One against me for making his daughter crazier. One against the Blood Cult Awareness Network for recommending me."

"That's absurd!"

She shrugged, then turned to catch the waiter's attention. After they'd ordered, she looked at Van Wyk again with an odd stare.

"Carleton… just what did happen that night?"

Van Wyk's face was blank, and his voice was emotionless when he responded. "I've told you. Her friend Raymond showed up. There was a struggle. He ran away." Laura peered intently into his eyes. Was his expression begging her to buy it? Daring her to disbelieve? Simply empty? She couldn't tell.

"I don't think you're being straight with me. I saw you bleeding that night… but two days later you were fine."

"Duane punched him in the nose. You know how much blood that can produce."

"Yes I do, but there was more than that. You were bleeding from your side."

"You must have misjudged."

"What does that tattoo on Duane's arm mean?"

"As far as I know, it's just a design."

"And the design you drew? The one you showed him? What's that?"

"I don't know what you're talking about."

"Carl, it's *me*! Please, you don't have to stonewall me! We're on the same side. *Please*, I just want to know the truth." Her eyes were bright, but she fought back her tears. They were silent while the waiter served their entrees, then Van Wyk looked directly at her.

"Dr. Jen… Laura. I have no doubt that we are on the same side. No doubt whatsoever. But there are elements to our mutual struggle that you are not equipped to handle. Duane and I are. This is through no credit of our own — only through an accident of fate. But the division is absolutely real. It is far, far better for you to *not know* certain things. I know you, and you are not one to look away as a crime is committed. If you knew, you would try to act. If you tried to act, you would die. Without a doubt. Duane and I will almost certainly die because of our involvement, but we at least have a chance."

"How can you know that?"

For a silent moment, he looked ancient — like a statue of some long-dead general, weary from keeping an ages-old vigil. "How can anyone know anything? There's no certainty — ask Heisenberg or Freud or Lacan. We can only use our best judgment."

"Who are you to judge for me?"

He shook his head.

"I'm sorry, Laura. If you think ill of me, I'll accept that rather than see you dead — or worse. You're doing a great deal of good with the network. Perhaps more than you realize. I don't want to see that undone by my secrets."

She reached across the table and took his hand. Tears were causing her makeup to run.

"Carleton, please let me in. *Please*. Whatever it is you're fighting, I'm fighting it too. I want to fight with my eyes open. Don't you see that this has *ruined* me?"

"You'll survive. You'll recover." He was thinking of people he'd seen truly ruined — souls destroyed, living only to obey the dead things, eager to degrade themselves or degrade others in hopes of a flicker of recognition from their masters. The image of Laura, bound, enslaved — no.

"All I could give you is the illusion of knowing. Like describing color to a blind person. Please believe me. If I dragged you into my life, it would be the basest form of selfishness." He gently pulled his cold fingers from hers. Stood. "Perhaps it's better that I go."

"I don't want to be alone."

"Again, you flatter me. Call Esme at BCAN, or Jay. They'll surely be better company than I." He swallowed. "I'll pay on the way out," he said finally.

Laura said, "Please be selfish for me," as he walked away. She didn't say it loudly and Van Wyk pretended he hadn't heard her. He found the waiter, paid cash and went out to the parking lot, but couldn't drive a block before he broke down crying. He cried so hard he had to curl into a ball.

*   *   *

September

Sometimes Van Wyk wished he drank. He recognized that, strictly speaking, he sometimes abused stimulants, but they were no relief for him. He simply used them when he couldn't permit himself to sleep. They weren't a refuge — the opposite, in fact. During the month following his supper with Laura, he took no drugs at all. He wrote a few prescriptions for chloral hydrate, but used it only to drug the servants of vampires so that he could move them easily to disposal areas. He followed his subjects and wrote in his notebooks.

Late one morning, Duane knocked on Van Wyk's apartment door. The older man saw through the peephole that the younger one wore a supple black leather jacket, new boots and an expensive-looking pair of sunglasses. Duane had never been handsome, and the fresh scar across his face didn't help. But he moved with a new confidence. Van Wyk opened the door.

"Hey, Doc. How's it going?"

"I'm well. Yourself?"

"Livin' large and kickin' ass. Feel like going out for some breakfast? My treat."

"I've eaten."

Duane smiled and looked over the top of his shades.

"Okay then. Wanna go kill a bloodsucker?"

Van Wyk's face was inscrutable. "Come inside," he said.

"It's one of those bastards from Rubies. Shit, I never thought that place would outlast BCAN."

"BCAN isn't dead yet."

"Well, those fuckers at Rubies are. They just forgot. Want in on a wake-up call?"

"Do you mean today?"

"I mean right now."

"This seems ill-considered."

"Oh yeah?" Duane reached into his coat and pulled out a blueprint.

"Here's the house. The security code is 66912 — keypads here and here. I got me an industrial cordless jigsaw in the car for the deadbolt here. I think Dracula's holed up in the old wine cellar... here."

"Hmm. Does 'Dracula' have any accomplices?"

"You mean, does it have any blood fucks? Yeah, four... but I just saw two of them catch the redeye to D.C. That leaves two, plus a private security cop who drives by every hour or so. But if we get there at quarter to eleven, he'll be five miles away, at the farthest part of his route."

"What about an escape route?"

"That's the nice part. He's right on the river, see? He's got a boat docked behind his place." Duane reached into his coat again, producing a map this time. "I figure we park here, walk a mile to the house, go in, do him and come out. If there's any kind of alarm, we play it by ear, either make a break for the car or grab the boat, cruise downstream here, get off and walk back to the car. If push comes to shove, we can sail to here, get off by the train yard and hop a freight."

"Very thorough. I'm tempted to ask why you need me."

"I don't have your eyes, Doc. I want this to go real easy. Also, this blood fucker is... Raymond. I haven't forgotten that you saw him right before he jumped us that night. If it wasn't for you, he'd probably be wearing my face for a jockstrap right now."

"You located his lair? Why didn't you tell me that from the beginning?"

"I... I know things didn't go well with Doctor Jenson — that what happened at the cabin got her in trouble and all. I wasn't sure how all that made you feel...."

Carleton looked down at the maps and schematics. "I'm in."

*   *   *

Two weeks later, Duane was getting a blow job when his phone rang. He tried to ignore it, but once his machine picked up and he heard Van Wyk's clipped and cultured tones, it broke his mood completely.

"Good day, Duane. It's 'Doc.' After our recent success, I believe I have some work that would interest you. You know my number. I'll await your call."

"What's wrong, sweetie? You just ignore that phone and concentrate on me here...."

"Nah, look... it's no good. The guy calling...."

The young woman, whose name was Honey (at least, that was all the name Duane knew) pouted sympathetically. "Bill collector?"

"No, just a, what, you know... a business associate."

"Well, he's gone now sugar. You want...?"

"Ah, I... don't think I can concentrate."

"You don't *need* to concentrate."

As it turned out, Honey was right. Duane waited until she was dressed, paid and gone before returning Van Wyk's call.

"Hi, Doc. What's the 411?"

"I'd prefer not to talk about it over the phone, but I believe I'm ready to make a move soon, if you would care to join me."

Duane laughed. "You sound like we're going on a date."

"How do you know that's not my intention?"

Duane agreed to come over and hung up smiling. "Did Doc Carl just make a *joke*?"

He wasn't smiling after Van Wyk explained what he had planned.

"Jeez, Doc... you want to make a move against Christoph? I think he's one of the real big shits in the local scene."

"All the more reason to deal with him — although I hadn't thought him so important. Perhaps you know something I don't? Have you been watching him?"

"A little, yeah."

"Excellent. I didn't spot you on my surveillance. Let us hope that they didn't, either."

Duane hooked a finger under his collar and scratched. "How many, you know, blood puppets?"

"None. He has two guards, but they're clean. His apartment building is fairly well guarded, but one of the cleaning staff has a habit. In return for some pills, I get his keys for twenty-four hours, along with the penthouse security code. Generally, the vampire goes out at night and the guards sleep. I propose to enter the apartment around three in the morning and drug any breakfast foods I find. Then I leave. There's an empty apartment on the third floor where I can wait for sunrise. With luck, by noon both guards will have eaten the drugged food and be out cold. If not, one will probably have gone by then. We enter, deal with any remaining and awake guards as necessary, and expose the master to the sun."

"I don't know, Doc…. Doing it in the middle of the day? In a busy apartment building? That's not your usual, you know, style. Kind of daring, isn't it?"

"I don't think it's rash, if that's your concern." One of Van Wyk's eyebrows bobbed up. "This is a bit of a reversal of roles, isn't it?"

"I just don't…. It doesn't feel right. No blood guards? Maybe you're missing something."

"That's certainly possible. That's why I want you along, Duane. I know how good you are in a fight. I want you at my back."

"Give me a day to look over the setup myself, you know? Then I'll decide."

"As you wish, but I pick up the key and code tonight. How can I contact you?"

"I got a pager now. I'll give you the number."

"I look forward to working with you again," Van Wyk said, and he meant it. But rationally, he felt that the best he could hope for would be never to see Duane again.

*   *   *

That night, just after nine o'clock, Van Wyk was surprised to hear his cell phone ring. He hadn't expected a call. Without taking his eyes from the apartment building across the street, he answered, "Hello?"

"Doc. You weren't at home."

"No. Pursuant to your concerns, I decided to do some more looking."

"Oh yeah? I've, uh, been in the building myself. Looking around."

"I saw you this time."

Van Wyk waited for Duane to respond.

"You did? Uh…."

"Did I give you this number?"

"No, I got it from Esme. You know, at BCAN." Duane sounded increasingly uncomfortable.

"So then, in or out?"

Duane sighed, cursed a little.

"Look, it's… aw, hell, you're too smart for me to lie. You know, Christoph offered me a lousy two G's to whack you? I told him he was underestimating you. Shit. Look, let's meet. We got a lot to talk about."

Van Wyk pondered whether he should turn off the phone and leave town immediately, get away from the vampire web that had somehow enmeshed Duane as well. But something made him a little foolish — or sentimental. Against his better judgment, he liked

Duane. Duane reminded him of Jared Shoemaker somehow. Being with Duane eased the pain Van Wyk felt whenever he thought of Jared.

"I'll page you," Van Wyk said and hung up.

*   *   *

One hour later, Duane knocked on Van Wyk's door. "It's open," the doctor said.

When Duane entered, Van Wyk was nowhere in sight. The hairs on the back of Duane's neck stirred, and then he saw. The old man sat in a folding chair, a brandy glass in one hand and a double-barreled shotgun in his lap. He had positioned himself so that the opening door would obscure his position.

"Doc, you don't need that."

The older man did not move.

"You've made your point. You can kill me if you want, okay?"

"Tit for tat, I suppose. You could have easily killed me days ago. Why didn't you? Price too low to bother?"

"Shit, it ain't like that…."

Van Wyk lowered the gun.

"Then suppose you tell me what it is like. I've already surmised that you're hiring out your skills. That's how you could get a new car and wardrobe. How you could afford designer sunglasses and prostitutes on a machinist's salary. That's how you knew so much about our last target's defenses — you had help from the inside." Van Wyk's voice, usually so calm and detached, was edged with contempt and a deep, deep rage. "Do you restrict yourself to assassinations? Or are you procuring nourishment for them as well?"

"Look, it's just one!"

"Ah, well, that's much preferable to you whoring your unearned abilities to a whole cemetery."

"Do you want to hear this or are you just going to sit there and be a smartass?"

Van Wyk took a deep breath.

"I want very much to know how you came to be working for Christoph."

"I know it sounds crazy…. Shit, he's seen us. He knows what we've been up to. He hasn't stopped us, though, cause we sort of… helped him. He hated Raymond — he hates the whole Rubies crowd. He contacted me to save my ass from some heavies Raymond sent after me. I guess Raymond saw enough at the cabin to ID me, but not you.

"Christoph's little 'heads up' saved my life, so the next time I heard him on the phone, I was willing to listen. He told me a lot."

"Including how to find Raymond and assassinate him."

"Yeah, but more than that. He's been telling me how vampires *work*, Doc. Did you know they don't have to drink blood?"

Van Wyk blinked.

"Every vampire I've observed has done so."

"Yeah, well, almost all of them do. But they don't *have* to. The blood is like gas for all their powers — the speed, the strength, making puppets. That's why they feed. Or the bad ones do, anyhow. But Chris isn't like that. He wants to see the predators — the ones who just want power and will kill to get it — he wants them off the streets. Just like you and I do. And he can help us do it, help us a *lot*."

"As he did with Raymond?"

"Yeah! He knows their schedules and their precautions…"

"And he pays well."

Duane looked at the floor.

"Shit, Doc. We risk our asses every time we do this. Why shouldn't we get something to show for it?"

"Do I really have a choice, Duane?"

"No, Doc, you do! I swear to God. I explained it to Chris, that you're a stand-up guy, real good at the job, and that you'd see reason. I didn't tell him your name or anything, and he doesn't know where you live. Look… you and me, we're a great team. But if you don't want to, that's cool. All I ask is that you stay out of our way. We won't mess with you, and you don't mess with us. Is that fair?"

"That's if I want out. What if I want in?"

Duane's eyes widened.

"You serious?"

"I'm not absolutely convinced, but all along I've wanted to know the truth of these matters. I'm not irrational or prejudiced. If I can observe directly, I'll surely gain a better insight into the nature of the rots. That's also the only fair way I can decide whether this Christoph can be trusted."

He frowned for a moment. "Duane… if things go bad, can I rely on you? If it comes to a choice between me and your patron, I mean?"

"Oh Doc, hey, absolutely! That's *not* going to happen, but even if it did, I'd pick you over a dead guy in an instant. Like that! But you'll see, Chris is really okay."

"I hope you're right. I really hope you are."

"I *am* right, Doc. Give me credit for some street smarts, okay?"

The old man sighed. "Would you like a drink? Have this one. I haven't had any yet. I'll pour myself another." Relief washed across Duane's face.

"Sure!" Duane said, accepting the glass from Van Wyk. "What's this you're having?"

"Brandy."

"Uh, brandy sounds fine. Listen, I have to make a call."

"To Christoph? I'd rather you didn't from here."

"Fine, have it your way." Duane tossed back most of the brandy snifter's contents in one swallow.

"You won't believe the money you're gonna make — and it's not like you didn't want to hunt vampires anyway, right?"

"I had no idea there was such competition among them."

"You wouldn't…. Yeah. If they could only… stick together… we'd be screwed." He frowned, smacked his lips. "That's…." The brandy snifter fell from Duane's hand and bounced off the carpet.

Van Wyk shook his head sadly and went to get his scalpel. Duane was too dangerous to leave alive, but disposing of him would be quite a chore. The old man knew a place where a dead body, drained of blood, could be left. By dawn, it would have vanished without a trace — or a police report. He started water running into the tub and didn't hear Duane staggering along the hallway. He smelled the hot metal of Duane's knife, instead, and barely had time to leap back before Duane lunged at him.

"Bastard!" Duane howled. Slowed by alcohol and chloral hydrate, his first slash went wild. As Van Wyk raised his scalpel, Duane stabbed downward, aiming for the older man's belly. He came in low, but still connected, cutting deep into Van Wyk's thigh. Van Wyk's scalpel scribbled down the side of Duane's face, but the young man tucked his head, protecting his neck. He stumbled backward, struggling to regain his footing, and seized the doctor's slender wrist. Duane pulled Van Wyk close, intending to impale him, and then the old man suddenly seemed much… taller. No, Duane realized, his own legs had collapsed. In fact, he was utterly numb from the waist down, but he still meant to kill the old bastard.

Even drugged and bleeding, Duane was fast. Van Wyk barely avoided his final lunge. The knife sank an inch into the paneling below the sink. It smoldered briefly, then cooled as Duane's grip on Van Wyk's wrist went slack.

Van Wyk stumbled to the toilet seat and sat down, gasping. The tub was still filling, and he splashed water onto his face. Wincing, he stood, irritated that he'd misjudged Duane's dosage. Now he would have to bandage his leg before killing his former ally. And Christoph surely knew where he lived, despite Duane's naïve assurances. Van Wyk glanced toward the hallway closet, which held his luggage, already packed. He hoped there would be enough time.

As Van Wyk stood there, Duane's eyes flickered. His lips moved as he fought the sedative: "Why?"

Van Wyk looked down at him, chest heaving.

"I used my best judgment."

HUNTER-BOOK JUDGE

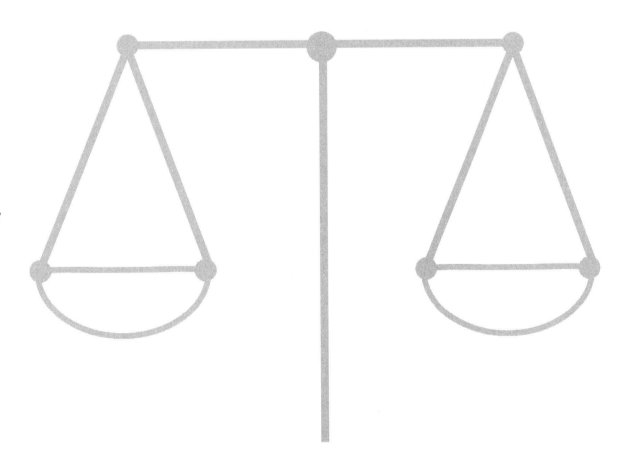

BY MICHAEL LEE, MIKE MEARLS, JOHN SNEAD AND GREG STOLZE

CREDITS

Authors: Michael Lee, Mike Mearls, John Snead and Greg Stolze
Developer: Ken Cliffe
Editor: Ed Hall
Devil's Advocate: Michael Lee
Art Director: Richard Thomas
Layout and Typesetting: Pauline Benney
Interior Art: Mike Danza, Langdon Foss, Brian LeBlanc
Front Cover Art: Tommy Lee Edwards
Front and Back Cover Design: Pauline Benney

WHITE WOLF HOCKEY SPECIAL THANKS

Tim "Voluntary Basis" **Avers** (Defense), for selecting himself to warm the bench.

Andrew "Robo-D" **Bates** (#6, Defense). "What's your name, Defenseman?"
"BATES."

Phil "La Fleur" **Boulle** (Wing), for knowing too much French stuff to shout at a Habs game.

Brian "Two Way" **Glass** (#84, Defense), for going both ways on the ice, too.

Rich "Sniper" **Thomas** (#13, Defense), for snagging two career goals in a single game.

Mike "Knee Braces" **Tinney** (#11, Goal), for learning that you can just leave your equipment at the arena… in the grass… all week.

WHITE WOLF PUBLISHING

735 PARK NORTH BLVD.
SUITE 128
CLARKSTON, GA 30021
USA

TABLE OF CONTENTS

INTRODUCTION

Now is the end come upon thee, and I will send mine anger upon thee, and will judge thee according to thy ways, and will recompense upon thee all thine abominations.
— Ezekiel 7:3

JUDGE, JURY AND EXECUTIONER

Hunter Book: Judge is a sourcebook to help you develop a better understanding of the Judge creed and its emerging role in the world of **Hunter: The Reckoning**. As a Judge, you decide the guilt or innocence of the supernatural, whether creatures commit atrocities against humanity or bear some glimmer of human decency and should be spared the gallows. You gather all the information you can about the creatures you observe — and from the allies you choose — but ultimately the decision to condemn or spare is yours. It's a terrible responsibility and one only you can bear. But what makes you tick? What consuming guilt, dangerous pride or extraordinary insight could make *you* the one to decide who's worthy? This book helps you decide, to determine who your Judge is, before and after the imbuing — and all the creed's new powers and rules don't hurt, either.

But just as you need to better understand your own Judge, you must understand hunter society as it emerges; the two are inextricably intertwined. As each of the newly imbued struggles to understand her new world, origins and purpose, she inevitably compares her experiences, philosophies and fears to those of others on the streets or on the Internet. At first, the recently awakened latch onto anyone who understands them; this new world is just too terrifying to contend with alone. In time, however, as more and more imbued dare meet and make overtures to find each other, individuals with similar attitudes and theories are attracted to one another and develop like-minded circles. These foundling social groups are the bases for what ultimately become the hunter creeds.

Yet, during hunters' emergence, many varied imbued can seem to have common goals. As the chosen make contact, try to understand their mutual condition and strive to work together, *similar* goals and *comparable* experiences can hide fundamentally different philosophies, whether about hunter purpose, the nature of the Messengers or the necessary fate of monsters. All hunters agree that the supernatural's hold on humanity must be broken, but not everyone agrees on how to accomplish this goal. Mutual experiences and mutual values turn out to be two very different things. Hunters can therefore be taken by surprise when a fellow "Judge" proves to be a militant Redeemer or a distracted Visionary. Sometimes, the chosen aren't even sure of their *own* ideals until they become immersed completely in the hunt.

It's only after the imbued become fully devoted to or even obsessed with the hunt that their approaches to it become purposeful and refined. Some become determined to save monsters' souls. Others want to see such creatures utterly destroyed. When this distillation of purpose is complete, the creeds as social classifications finally arise. Judge recognizes Judge and Martyr recognizes Martyr, all through the creeds' codified values, intentions and goals in the hunt.

When will hunters achieve such social structure? It could take months or years as the imbued struggle to understand themselves and then each other. The fact that so many edges seem to be shared by the chosen of various perspectives and personalities doesn't help, either. Once creeds as institutions are finally acknowledged, however, the hunt may finally gain the momentum it needs to overcome the supernatural, once and for all. Or perhaps such cumbersome and fractious divisions will be the hunt's undoing, as imbued fall to infighting and politics rather than upholding their higher purpose.

Ultimately, the course of your chronicle and your Storyteller's vision decide when the creeds become widely recognized in your game. In the meantime, your Judge's fully developed identity helps define his own society.

PERSPECTIVES

The opinions, theories, information and outlooks expressed in this book are presented primarily in three distinct "voices." These Judge narrators typify the spectrum of personalities throughout the creed as a whole. Each of these people presents his or her own take on the origins, tactics, relations and ultimate fate of Judges, and on hunters in general.

The creed and its members' views evolve constantly as Judges try to define themselves in a world they no longer understand. With no other frame of reference, the chosen often resort to the ideas, values and philosophies they possessed before their transformation. No two Judges have the same thoughts about their origins, for example. Thus, the *questions* the imbued ask about themselves and their world—not any specific *belief system*—best illustrate their individual and collective identity. After reading this book, you should have a sense of the drives and ambitions that inspire and motivate various Judges. You should sense why these people feel compelled to weigh the good and bad in monsters, and what influences their relations with other imbued. We also hope that you're inspired to develop your character's identity and beliefs fully, to make him just as compelling in his pursuit of justice.

HOW TO USE THIS BOOK

Hunter Book: Judge broadens the World of Darkness as creed members perceive it and offers insights into the hunter psyche. It also offers new rules and powers for use by Judges and possibly other creed members. This book can therefore help you better understand your character and elaborate upon her.

Chapter 1: Hunter Origins explores the nature of monsters, the Messengers and Judges, and seeks to explain why the imbued receive their gift — or curse.

Chapter 2: The Hunt covers Judges' approach to their calling and what they do to decide the relative worth of a monster's soul (if any such thing can exist).

Chapter 3: Hunter Ties describes Judges' relations with themselves and other creeds.

Chapter 4: Our Future presents creed member's efforts to define their purpose and destiny in the World of Darkness.

Chapter 5: New Rules offers more rules, edges and equipment for use by Judges and perhaps by hunters of other creeds.

Chapter 6: Presiding Judges details newly imbued Judges who are ready for play. This chapter also profiles creed members who have acquired reputations through word of mouth or the Internet.

LEXICON

Judges bring their own unique perspectives to the hunt. They seek to perceive the relative worth of a creature (or a person or another hunter) in hopes of accomplishing the greatest possible good for the world—and so reclaim it in the name of propriety and decency. If a being displays unremitting hatred or malice, an arbiter is quick to put it down or condemn it for others to dispatch. If a creature exhibits remorse for its actions or disdain for its corrupt state, it might be spared and perhaps even left for others to nurture back into the human fold. Such evaluation requires that Judges consider each subject individually, based on a mediator's own sense of idealized right and wrong, good and evil. Although a Judge might uphold virtually unattainable levels of virtue by which to measure a being, he still looks upon each defendant as an individual, rather than dismissing all demons or bloodsuckers as irredeemably corrupt.

Since Judges think in terms of the individual, they tend not to develop or use terms that apply to groups or that subject single beings to preconceived notions. Judges therefore have not demonstrated slang or any list of hunting terms characteristic to them alone. Doing so would defy their purposes.

When playing your Judge character, take pains to avoid gross classification of creatures, people and even other imbued (the very notion of hunter "creeds" might be ludicrous, for example). You might even point out to characters of other creeds the dangers of such gross generalization. It's easy to call something a "monster" because it does not belong to *nature*, but mere classification of a being as supernatural is not sufficient for most Judges to sentence it to death.

SOURCE MATERIAL

Movies, TV shows, comics and books are full of characters who consider actions, weigh decisions, plan actions, coordinate fellows and seek the best results for their harsh worlds. A Judge doesn't have to be all about black-and-white laws or justice at the end of a gun. The following resources contain excellent characters after whom you could model your Judge.

Saving Private Ryan: Tom Hanks' character bears the enormous responsibility of his unit's mission and well-being, and he personally seeks to achieve the greater good of ending the war with a minimum of bloodshed. Not only does he decide to spare enemy soldiers, he elects to sacrifice his own men and himself for the salvation of others. The pressures of his decision-making manifest in his psychological paralysis.

Brimstone: The main character of this show, a damned cop returned to Earth to recapture souls escaped from Hell, is no Avenger or Martyr. He brings no wrath or personal sacrifice to his appointed mission. Rather, he attends to each "target" in turn, letting some go and contending with the unbridled malice of others. Indeed, his time on Earth is an opportunity to deal with the good and evil still among the living — an opportunity to find salvation.

The Equalizer: It's been years since this show's network run ended, but it remains an A&E standby. Edward Woodward's character was the epitome of Judge. An ex-government agent, he breaks away to run his own public-assistance business. "If you're in trouble and you have nowhere else to turn…." The old dude kicks ass, separates the deserving from the undeserving and dispenses justice when the System can't.

Highlander: The Series: Painful as it is to suggest such a cliché of genre culture, Duncan McLeod would make an excellent Judge. He's peaceful by nature and seeks to help people who deserve it, but is quick to dole out his fair share of violence against those mortals or immortals who reject peace.

That '70s Show: "What?" you ask. Dismiss almost everyone on the show except Red Forman. Now make his surroundings 100-percent drop-dead serious. He's the ideal blue-collar regular guy and he has unmitigated standards of right and wrong, proper and improper, wise and foolish. Add to all that his penchant to tell people when they screw up and you've got the personification of a Judge and of **Hunter** itself.

JUDGE, NOT VISIONARY

Judges' calling doesn't involve just weighing the worth of creatures, people and hunters. Their responsibility is much greater. Judges tend to be the information gatherers among the imbued. Where fools rush in, they collect intelligence, observe patterns and search for weaknesses. Not that collecting data makes Judges ineffectual; they strike when they believe it will be most effective and efficient, with a minimum of harm to themselves, their allies and unwitting people. Information gathering also grants arbiters the strength to act with confidence when they don't know all the details about a situation or subject that they'd like to know. Previous experience and extrapolation from past successes (which *were* based on amassed intelligence) contribute to a kind of intuition on which Judges may rely.

By virtue of studying and preparing, Judges make ideal leaders of imbued in the field, on the hunt. Their knowledge, experience and planning allow them to coordinate other hunters, to help those people get the job done and to survive.

Finally, Judges approach their mission with personal ideals of right and wrong. These ideals are often upheld rigorously, for the mediator herself and for any imbued under her guidance. She might decide that robbing from or hurting harmless people is not an acceptable price for condemning or exonerating a creature. She might observe two "demons" fighting and decide that one is more deserving than the other, because the worthy "beast" doesn't actually feed upon people but has the chance to contribute to human society. These ideals of right and wrong therefore help a Judge aspire to accomplish the greatest good for the world.

All of these qualities define your character as a Judge and make her different from a Visionary. Visionaries are the contemplators among the imbued, constantly looking to the horizon to see were the hunt leads and in what direction it might be taken to liberate humanity. They consider the war as a whole and choose actions based on their far-flung conclusions. As such, Visionaries also make good leaders for the chosen in giving other imbued direction and purpose.

Although Judge and Visionary agendas sound similar, the creed members are very different. Judges are the facilitators of the here and now. They act and think in the relatively short term as they try to solve the problems immediately before them. Visionaries, meanwhile, take the long view and ponder dilemmas or possibilities that might have no bearing whatsoever on, say, that mob of shambling dead currently plaguing the city. Such differences of opinion on necessity and performance can strain Judge and Visionary relations, but can also strengthen them. A Judge can take charge of actions "in the field," as a military officer does, whereas a Visionary gains some distance from the front lines and can plan the campaign, like a general.

So when you play your Judge, don't let her get *too* caught up in theory, philosophy or pondering. A judge delivers justice upon the supernatural, and justice waits for no man… or monster.

CHAPTER 1: HUNTER ORIGINS

*He shall judge the poor of the people, he shall save the
children of the needy, and shall break in pieces the oppressor.*
— Psalms 72:4

OPENING STATEMENTS

From: listserver
Subject: Welcome

As the subject line says, welcome to judgmentday.list. As you already know by virtue of being here, the Drumskin web site is a scam. It's a real place, all right, but it's really just a convenient cover for what I and a few others have seen about how things *really are* in the world. You've probably seen *something*, too, maybe a few days or even a few weeks ago. Trust us, we know what you've been going through. Trying to understand it, you might have gone online and run a few search terms that seemed right or that just stuck in your head. That's what we were hoping for. That's how you found the bogus site. You probably emailed me when the sign there sent a shiver up your spine and you finally felt that something was *right*.

I've already emailed back to you individually. Since you were invited onto this list, you recognized something about yourself in that symbol. To me it means "balance," in terms of somehow serving or achieving balance against what we know lurks out there. I don't know how I get that feeling. I just do and I can't shake it.

Others tell me the symbol means "justice" or "deliverance" or even "judgment" to them. I guess those work for me in a way, too. The last one struck me in particular and was inspiration for this list's name, given the course the world seems to be on.

If you came here solely for the religious applications of the site's name or search terms and managed to get this far, don't bother going any further. You'll only be confused. There are other strictly Christian discussion groups out there. *Our* "judgment day" is not *your* "Judgment Day." You won't find any Apocalyptic horsemen or pearly gates here. At least, not yet.

Despite that rather cryptic introduction, this list is a little more sedate than some of the others for people with our "interests." Yes, there are other people like you who know things, and other sites like this one that try to make sense of it all. We won't send you to other sites for security reasons, but you'll find them. You found this group, didn't you?.

If you just want to post manifestoes and brag, this isn't the place for you. We're looking for day-to-day (or moment-to-moment) techniques for dealing with "issues," and larger strategies for how justice can be served on a broad scale. We want to know how you've made decisions and how you've come to conclusions, how you've given direction to others like us, and how you gather information when we generally seem to know so little about *how things are*. Beyond that, topics can range fairly widely. Use your own discretion. People are generally polite here, so there's not a lot of need for net-copping.

Another major reason for this list is concern for the security of the largest of our lists. It seems pretty stable now, but there have been remote hardware problems and even cases of imposture. While I can't ensure that the same won't happen on this list, I feel that the more of them that we have going, the better off we are. Otherwise, all our eggs are in one basket.

Your subscription to judgmentday has been processed, but before you start posting, let me offer some advice and assurances.

Your real email address will never appear in any post, unless you put it in the body of a message. The same is true for your given name. Please *do not* send your email address to anyone on this list, *ever*. (My hotmail account is under a false name.) If someone attempts to assemble a full list of us or others like us internet-wide, I'll leave it to individuals to decide if addresses should be forwarded.

Likewise, never give your real name or real address. Make up a handle for yourself. It's proprietary. If you pick "Fisher," there'll never be another "Fisher" (unless someone picks "Fisher2" or something). The numerical place holders of the main list are not needed here. Some people bring their other handles onto judgmentday, but you don't have to. You can call me "Listserver." No one needs to know any more than that.

PRECEDENTS

To: judgmentday.list@hunter-net.org
From: justme
Subject: <no subject provided>

Uh, hi. I guess I'm not supposed to put my name in here, which is weird. I got on this mailing list from the web page with the symbol - the tattoo thing. I haven't been reading long. I just signed on to hunter.net. I'm "JustMe322" over there. I haven't posted there yet. Those people seem like they're all over the place.

Did Crusader and Ripsaw really do those things that I read? I mean, I haven't "retired" or "terminated" anyone yet, and I don't really know if I could. I don't know anything about fighting, and I don't know anything about all these things I've started seeing. My "first time" wasn't really that great, either.

I was at the mall one evening after school with my friend Jen and we were waiting for her sister to pick us up. (My mom's car was in the shop, so she took mine to go see a patient.) So we're at the mall door and there's this guy there, maybe a little younger than us? Weird looking, like he was sick or something. I couldn't really put my finger on what it was, but he gave me the creeps. But Jen thought he was cute for some weird reason. So she's, like, talking to him while we're waiting, when I heard this voice. I thought it was on the loudspeaker at first. It said "the dead are at war" and I was looking around for where it was coming from right before Jen started screaming.

So what I could suddenly see was that the kid was dead. Like, pale and not breathing or anything. And he was trying to get away from this other dead guy who'd come from nowhere. This old guy looked deader, if that makes sense. He was all rotted and messed up, and he was just whaling on the kid. I shouted something. I know I did because my throat was sore later, but I sure don't remember what I yelled. And then my mom was there. I don't know where she came from. She said later that her patient missed the session, so she decided to shop for my uncle's

birthday. Anyhow, people were running everywhere and my mom started yelling out the window. Jen just jumped into the car and mashed her face down in the back seat.

With us yelling at him, I think the old guy looked kind of confused. I don't know what I was thinking. I grabbed the kid and pulled him into the car. I guess he seemed like, the underdog, you know. I just couldn't stand to watch him get beat up. The old guy didn't like that, I think. He punched through the back door window - smash - just like that. All three of us were screaming and my mom floored it and squealed out of there.

We were like, miles away before my mom pulled over at an IHOP. She was breathing deep and trying to be calm, and then Jen went totally nuts. "He's dead!" she yelled. Mom tried to take the kid's pulse and he was cold. Not to mention that he was all torn up. It was gross. He had these big cuts all over his face and arms, but they weren't bleeding. He was really pale. Then all of a sudden, his eyes popped open. It was like the scene in "Scream" where you think the killer's dead but he jumps out at you? We all got scared like that.

He was in the back seat between me and Jen, and his mouth opened with these two giant fangs. He went right for Jen's throat. She pulled the door latch and fell out, and I jumped out after her, trying to get him off her. I think he was weak from getting beat, because I drug him off her pretty easy, and then he started fighting me.

I'm kind of shaky about what happened next. It all happened really fast, but mom helped me remember. She smashed him with her briefcase, one of those big metal ones. Then she dropped it or he took it away from her somehow and knocked her over. So I grabbed a rock from this flower bed and I stood up and bashed him. Then he turned on me again and hit me with the briefcase. The corner of it right on my head.

I woke up in the hospital. Mom was there and crying like a baby. Everything was really blurry. It still is. I've got a dent in my temple about the size of a nickel. The doctor says he thinks something in my eye - the white part, I guess - got wrecked and he doesn't know if they can fix it.

So that's what happened to me during my "imbuing," if that's what it's called. Jen got away with nothing but bruises. So did my mom. But Jen can't recognize any of the symbols like the one on your site. She even has trouble remembering everything that happened that

To: judgmentday.list@hunter-net.org
From: traveler72
Subject: Re: <no subject provided>

justme wrote:

>Did Crusader and Ripsaw really do those things

Yes. I was there. I won't work with Ripsaw again, and I don't think Crusader will either. Crusader may not seem much better, but I don't think he hurts people. He tries not to, anyhow. I think he only likes people in theory. I have mixed feelings about Crusader. He claims to care about people so much, but when you meet him, all that comes across is a mix of hatred and intense self-control. He's scary. But very good at what he does.

Ripsaw is just a butcher. Stay away from him and make sure anyone you care about does, too.

night - worse than me. I saw the symbol on the tattooing sign, and it looked familiar, but it didn't mean much to my mom. She drew another one, which looked, I dunno, "right" to her somehow, but not as much to me.

I've also found that if I concentrate real hard, I can make my vision get clear again. Anyone know what that's all about?

To: judgmentday.list@hunter-net.org

From: tarjiman220

Subject: Introduction

[Greetings, friends. I have been able to translate the first of the posts from the gentleman who uses the title "Warden." One of my colleagues in [censored] suggested that the English lists, which seem the largest, might have interest in his comments, so I send this to hunter.list and the others like it. I cannot tell you where "Warden" is from, but it is an industrialized nation and he is an intelligent and educated man.]

I have observed a number of lists from around the world. Though I am not fluent with many languages, it is possible to ascertain some common factors about all our interactions, even from piecing together occasional words. The greatest questions I have seen asked are: Who are we? What are we doing? And why? These are questions that mankind has asked since our origins. They have always plagued us. Yet these existential uncertainties take on a new urgency when one must account for the existence of murderous supernatural beings.

Where did we come from? I cannot pretend to give an ultimate answer to this question, but has anyone ever? I can, however, recount my own

"awakening" and theorize about what it means, and what it might show about how we are chosen.

I am the warden of a prison for violent or incorrigible criminals. My office looks over the exercise yard, and one day I heard a commotion. There is a certain music to the sound of the convicts. Over the years, I have become adept at hearing the difference between ordinary talk and trouble. On the day I awoke, it was definitely trouble. I looked out the window and saw a monster, for lack of a better term. It was tall, covered with thick black hair, and it was ripping a convict apart in sight of all.

I ran toward the yard, giving orders [??? I do not know the word.] as I went. By the time I got there, the situation was much worse. Two guards fired at it from the walls. Four guards were dead in the yard. Others were running, as were most of the convicts. I think those were the wise ones. Five convicts attempted to fight the creature, grabbing [Another unknown term for me. Clubs?] from the dead guards. I could see there was little good I could do from the ground, so I got a rifle and joined the guards on the wall. I fired many times before it finally died. Of the five inmates who tried to fight it, three survived and were still striking the carcass when we arrived. Everyone who had seen the beast was hysterical, with the exception of those three inmates, the two guards who had fired from the wall, and myself. We needed tear gas and fire hoses to restore order, but when the fog cleared, I learned several things.

First: When dead, the monster appeared to turn into a human shape, as if the monstrous form were not its first or that the human one was a ruse. Specifically, it could be identified as one of our new inmates. I cannot tell you his name without endangering myself. Let us call him "Frank." He was serving a term for aggravated assault.

Second: Only the two guards, three convicts and myself remembered the incident clearly. Everyone else asked presented hazy and contradictory [dreams?]. One inmate described Frank fighting another convict and the guards overreacting and opening fire. Never mind that guards carry no firearms in the yard, and that the injuries inflicted by "Frank" were clearly gashes, not bullet wounds.

The other guards who witnessed the event were no more coherent. They remembered Frank seizing a guard's rifle and thought other convicts had helped him in what was clearly an escape attempt. This, again, despite the care we take to keep weapons out of the exercise yard, even out of the hands of guards there.

Third: Two of the convicts and one of the guards later confessed individually that they "heard voices." The guard apparently heard "He is the beast." One convict claimed to hear, "You have the Power" and another, "Death walks hidden," whatever those might mean. I believe I retained my senses during the episode, yet I cannot say that I heard any particular voices apart from those of the people I worked with. I therefore cannot confirm or deny any of these claims.

Fourth: The three convicts, two guards and myself seemed to develop what I can now call "enhanced sight," based on what I have pieced together of it from other accounts. I thought perhaps that what I witnessed in the yard that day was an isolated event. It was certainly the most extraordinary and daunting thing I had ever experienced. It was thus a tremendous shock when we perceived that one of the guards on the night shift was, in best terms, not human. He was our second elimination.

Some of the guards present when the first being appeared were good men, but to my knowledge they did not gain any special insights or "capabilities." The rest of us have, inexplicably. Of the three prisoners who were awakened, we have an arsonist, a rapist and a murderer. This convinces me that the difference between those who become awakened and those who do not is not based on any kind of morality. I suspect the difference is simply this: We who acted were armed to act. Those who fled or who merely stood appalled were not, because they did not have the capacity to act within them or they were simply not selected to do so.

To: judgmentday.list@hunter-net.org
From: thomas
Subject: Paths

Many of you on this list are going to discover that, as you band together to follow whatever path you feel lies before you, that someone will step up first and lead the way. He may be chosen by you, selected by our "patrons" by some means, or perhaps even elected by himself to organize hunts, assign duties and decide the course that you should follow. He will know the nearest destinations on his path, and how to contend with roadblocks that occur. He will be a good navigator, but ultimately will not know what lies at the end of his journey, or perhaps even care. For him, the journey may be as important as the destination. Perhaps it is. These would-be leaders can be our greatest allies or greatest enemies.

From sentiments I've seen expressed here, I suspect that many of you could be these very people. Rather than attack or hold out a hand instinctively, you seem to consider the beings you encounter, weigh the choices you face and search for the greatest possible good, whether for man or monster. You therefore bear a burden. Under proper direction, we hunters can be a potent force for improving this world. Under the wrong leadership, we could rival the creatures of the night for the sorrow we could cause. You may be the ones to help choose the way, at least in the short term.

What follows is an archive of e-mails and journal entries sent to me by the one who calls himself Solomon. You might recognize some of these posts; he sent messages to at least one list. I think he wanted to convince me of the error of my own ways, in hopes that I'd fall into line and follow blindly into the short-sighted future he sought to create. Read this and learn of those who might lead you, or whom you might become.

I sign off using the name I'm given in my very brief cameo in this sad story. All I can do is hope there are more Tarjimans out there, helping others find a better way where the Solomons have fallen to the wayside.

— Thomas

This is my first post here, so I should at least let you know where I'm coming from. I ran my family's business before I learned the truth. Let me tell you something: if you think there's a lot of them in positions of power, you're right. It's not like they're rooted everywhere like weeds. It's more like they know exactly which spots to pick — the ones that are easily defended and that give them access to all levels of power. I saw dead things, I saw things that were just different, and I knew that I had to get out of the business world. I liquefied my assets, made some noise about retiring to Europe, and cut all contacts to my old friends. They couldn't see the truth, and I didn't want to live their lies anymore.

I'm living partly in the streets, partly in cheap hotels now. Twice a week, I wash up and go online at a public computer. That's about all you need to know about me, a "lowlife" with enough cash socked away to buy a dozen houses. As you can see, I don't believe in half measures. We have to be decisive.

I don't normally talk about myself like this, but I get the feeling that it's important to some of you to know where we all stand. I never won any philosophy awards in school, and I don't expect that to change here. My philosophy has always been that beliefs are useless unless they're put into action. But it's critical that I communicate with you, if only to prevent you from falling in with some of the wrong-headed thinkers out there.

There's not a lot that we can take for granted about our situation, but we do seem to know this: Some people see monsters. Some people see ghosts. Sometimes the newly imbued do the right thing and take a monster down. Other times, they try to talk to it. There's no pattern, no guiding force here. Take a look at the members of this list; we can hardly agree on anything. If there is something supposedly organizing us, I'd be more inclined to call it a guiding stupidity than a guiding intelligence.

We can theorize all we want, but even if we come up with an explanation that makes us happy, we still don't know enough to say anything for sure.

Think back to your life before your change. If I told you a year ago that the world was run by dead people, you would have thought I was a crackpot. I'm sure that if anyone on this list ever came up with the truth, we'd never agree that it was right or we'd all dismiss the guy as nuts. Since we know so little, we have to draw lines and place things that are beyond our control on one side, and things that we can change on the other. Some of you might find comfort thinking about the big how's and why's of our situation. I have to think that making plans for taking out rots or gathering intelligence on skin changers is a better use of our time. Looking at the big picture is fine, but we need to see it with a practical eye.

We bear a terrible responsibility. It's unthinkable that we would do anything but carry it through to the best of our abilities. I will only deal with that which I can see, touch or experience directly. Given that we went through life for so long completely ignorant of the truth of our existence, I don't see any point in trying to ponder the unknowable. As far as I can see, the source of our powers has no bearing on our mission. There's no outside power telling me what to do. I'm acting on the same beliefs and skills that made me a success in the business world.

If you found yourself outside a burning building and people inside were screaming for help, would you stop and wonder why you happened to be near that building at that point in time or would you do something and save people? That's how I look at our situation. I'm still my own person. I still like chocolate cake and I still hate *Seinfeld*. I'm just not as ignorant about the world as I was before.

Journal Entry 1

My brother is dead.

That decadent bastard's immoral life finally caught up with him. Mother and Father were always lenient with him. I think I was the only one who was not surprised when he was forced to leave Harvard because of his grades. I remember when he used to try to get me to "help" him with his schoolwork back at Andover. That little snot, with the girls always looking at him and laughing at his stupid little jokes and the guys always clustering around him, soaking up the glory he won on the baseball field.

I remember teaching him to throw a baseball. Father was never around, as usual. I remember that even as a five-year-old he had a great arm.

I can't dwell on that now. I have to remember when he came to me, finally back from his "vacation" in Europe. I should have been suspicious when he asked to meet at the office after midnight. What would have happened if I hadn't been so quick to write it off as an eccentricity? I can't think like that; I was going to work that late anyway. No matter where we were when we met — it could have been in the middle of Quincy Market — the flames would have shown me that he wore death like one of his stylish new suits, lording it over poor, unstylish me.

I always get a little too sentimental for my own good in these diaries. I have to remember that he was no longer Roderick by then but a sickening imitation. Something killed him and possessed his body. That's the only explanation. Roderick was human. That thing I killed wasn't.

THE SOURCE OF THE IMBUING

To: judgmentday.list@hunter-net.org
From: tarjiman220
Subject: Our Source

[I further my correspondence with Warden. His English is not good, so I continue to translate. This message is sent to a variety of lists again.]

I have been observing the awakened in my prison. I choose not to share their names, for reasons you comprehend. Instead, I will refer to them by letters (for the guards) and by their crimes (for the convicts).

Guard H has developed two different potentials, for lack of a better term. One is a capacity to inflict deadly harm with something thrown, such as a stone or one of the prison's dining trays. Of course, such items would cause harm unto themselves, but the damage Guard H can inflict seems disproportionate to the items concerned. Additionally, if he touches a person, he can create a trail that he describes as smoke, but which is apparently invisible to most. With great concentration, I can sometimes see a faint image of the streamer he describes, as can Guard S.

Guard S shares with me an ability to perceive subtleties about beings and people, but not in the minute ways that I do. I do not fully understand his capability. It seems [intuitive?] rather than factual. He furthermore has the ability to impair the advance of a dangerous creature. He describes it as a force that flows from him, that pushes back any unnatural thing. Interestingly, this "rejection" is shared with one of the convicts.

The prisoner I shall name Murder possesses a similar protective capacity as Guard S, though he does not claim to have S's special perception. In addition, when Murder strikes a clubbing blow with an ordinary object, his weapon appears extremely effective and dangerous, much like Guard H's thrown objects. Also, I have seen Murder ignite cloth with a metal object, and during his awakening episode he inflicted burns upon the hairy creature by striking it with a weight from a barbell.

The second convict, Rape, has proven difficult and [churlish?]. He refuses to demonstrate his powers, claiming that he can only access them when needed, "not to be a spectacle," he insists. Given the evidence he once put on the body of a target, he seems to be able to make his hands corrosive or damaging in some fashion.

The final prisoner, Arson, does not possess the aggressive powers of the other convicts. Instead, he has developed an astonishing ability to avoid harm, simply by yelling at it. I myself have seen him turn aside knife thrusts and the claws of monsters with a simple shout.

This array of abilities bears directly, I believe, upon the question of our nature and origin. As we have learned through difficulty in our first months of operation, these skills are specific. They have details. After careful consideration, I conclude that these are not the kinds of crude [mutations?] one sees from purely blind, evolutionary happenstance. Take H, for example. His abilities suit him well for a role like a picador's. He can follow a prey at a distance and harass it readily, without putting himself at great risk. Murder, on the other hand, is more like a matador. His defensive ability allows him to repel a creature's assault, while his attack delivers great damage, but only at close quarters. Guard S and Arson are both well suited to follow and observe, but are less able to finish the task.

Sometimes in nature one sees this sort of specialization. In hive insects, perhaps, where a different diet makes this one a drone, that one a queen. But to my knowledge, this sort of "natural role" is not found in a higher animals, and certainly does not occur spontaneously. I therefore speculate that our awakening is not natural. At least, that it is not part of the "nature" of man that we once knew.

A different hypothesis is religious. A number of posters on the list in my language explain their episodes of awakening in religious terms. I am on shaky ground when it comes to addressing religion (as are we all, I suppose), but this explanation does not appeal. The "blessing" of a vicious multiple rapist is antithetical to me.

It is disturbing that a plausible religious explanation for us has come from Rape himself. After an early mission, Arson and Murder were both injured. While the guards and I were occupied with that crisis, Rape departed by stealth. I found him before he was able to remove his electronic tracking anklet but not before he had acquired some [hallucinogens?], which he ingested immediately.

It was under this influence that he shared his theory. (Indeed, he could have been making it up.) According to Rape, we were all awakened, not by angels, but by devils that take issue with the current ruler of the world (who is, of course, a devil himself). We were chosen then, not based on merit, but because we are useful. It matters not to the devil if you are a good or bad man, as long as you will hit the other devil's followers hard.

Yet this proposition does not satisfy me. It seems too elaborate. If these beings can give us the powers to fight their enemies, why do they not simply do their own fighting? This is the central puzzle with the [Again, I do not know the word. I believe he refers to the Heralds here]. When we answer this, we may be able to answer our greater questions.

In the end, I must take refuge in agnosticism, as I always have on matters of the spirit. On those subjects about which a person cannot speak, that person must remain silent.

This is not to say that I doubt that we have a mission. I can see for myself the savagery of our new world. When I see a creature that feeds on sorrow inhabiting the body of a charity worker, I do not pause before taking the obvious right action. Neither do I question whose hand took the scales from my eyes.

Mom's got some interesting ideas about where all these funky powers come from. She's a psychologist, so she's heard about some pretty weird stuff. Like one lady who had multiple personalities that supposedly gave off electric shocks. She said that it got so bad they wouldn't let her use the phone if she'd been "switching" a lot in a session - she'd short it out!

Then there's just the general weirdness of hypnosis, with people talking languages they never knew and remembering things they shouldn't have been able to. Mom's pretty skeptical. She thinks it's really easy for a hypnotist to give out clues about what they want without realizing it, but even she says she's seen some things she can't explain.

A bunch of people have said they think there have been hunters before. That kind of makes sense to me. I mean, seeing what the creatures out there can do, there'd have to be something keeping them in control. Otherwise, wouldn't they just totally take over everything?

Maybe in the olden days, people knew how to fight monsters and we've all forgot somehow. Maybe the imbuing is just remembering the past where you knew how to fight monsters. I still don't know why it's all happening now. Crystal23 on the big list keeps talking about how it's a new age. I always thought that astronomy was kind of bull, but then again I never believed in bogeymen before either.

I'm reading the old posts from the guy who was looking for some scientific answer, but that doesn't make sense to me. Now that my sight is all messed up, I've got to wear big thick glasses, right? So when I put the glasses on, my vision goes from being blurry to being clear. Or I can put on that "special" sight and see clearly then too. But here's the weird thing. When I concentrate, I can see clearly through the glasses or without them. It's like they're just window glass. That just shouldn't be, should it? I mean, in physics they talk about how glasses distort light and curve it. If it's curved right it should look differently through glasses, no matter if my vision is clear or blurry. But it doesn't. With the special thing, it looks just the same.

So, where did I get this weird thing, and does it make me like people who were like us before?

I can look at what I know about the imbuing, as I've seen it called, and I can tell you one thing: I have no idea why it happened, or what caused it. All I can do is deal with the aftermath.

We appear to have had a choice. Some of us saw the truth and decided to do something about it. Some of us just stood there and let a something terrible have its way. When I saw the thing, I knew it was evil and I took steps to destroy it. It was an almost instinctual reaction, like how the densest animal knows enough to be afraid of fire.

We all seem to have made that choice, given the relatively common experiences we account. Kill the dead thing... again. I did it. You did it. It wasn't God. It wasn't Mother Earth. It wasn't Father Christmas. It was us.

I don't care where the voices come from, and I don't care who gave us these powers. We made our decision to start this fight, and it's up to us to carry through and end it. You're here because you chose to be here. If you didn't want it, you'd still be in the dark. Our apparent abilities let us fight the monsters. What we need to do now is formulate a concrete strategy for identifying and destroying the things, not posture and philosophize.

Journal Entry 3

I have found a community of the "imbued," as they call themselves, on the internet and have joined an e-mail list that distributes news and opinions of our activities. I can already see that some on the list are unreachable. I've decided to not expose the full extent of my activities and plans. First, I can't trust that the members of this list are all normal. There has been a lot of talk about security breaches. Second, as was true for humanity at large, so is it true for these "imbued": Many are fools and many are malicious. I still don't know if willful evil is worse than evil born of ignorance or stupidity.

BEAR WITNESS

I don't know anything about all these kinds of monsters that people are talking about. I've only seen a couple, the two I saw when I got imbued and one where I work. I've got a job at a video store. Not a big chain, just an independent store. Anyhow, a lot of people come through, so I've been keeping an eye out with that concentration looking. I spotted one and today I had to do more than just look.

There's this one woman. She lives close by and comes in fairly often. She looks kind of sad, always rents comedies. Her name's Edith. So after I got hit in the head and started seeing things funny, I took a special look at her and saw that she had this "thing" floating around her. I don't know, I guess it was a ghost. No one else could see it, that's for sure, because it was all messed up. It had a smashed head with eyes pointing different ways and all bloody. The first time I saw it I had to run to the bathroom and puke. I told the manager it was something I'd eaten and she sent me home early.

I was ready for it the next time Edith came in. I kind of got her address and phone number off the computer. I took a walk by her place - it's only about three blocks from where I work. If I looked close, I could see in the window.

She was sitting on the couch by herself, looking really tired, and that invisible thing was sitting right next to her, like they were on a date. I don't think she knew it was there. I can't say why I know that. I've gone by when she's not there, and sometimes the ghost is there. Sometimes it isn't.

Anyway, yesterday she came in with this funny looking guy. Kind of like John Tutturro, sort of like Steve Buscemi. They seemed like they were on a date or something. She looked happy or at least kind of cheerful. The ghost was with them, too, sort of scowling as far as I could tell. They had some Chinese food from the place next door, and weren't driving. So I got Neal, who works with me, to cover for me while I snuck out to see what happened.

They were walking back to her apartment, around the back of the store. They were taking the street, which is the long way around this undeveloped area with no pavement or buildings. I went over the fence and got ahead of them. I couldn't hear what they were saying, but the guy was laughing. He had a weird laugh - not a "ha ha" but one of those really up and down laughs. She must have said something really funny.

They were walking across the parking lot to her apartment. I was looking with the real clear sight and I saw the ghost reach down and yank the guy's shoelace. It took the guy a couple steps to notice, and while he was doing that, the ghost ran over to this parked truck. As the guy was tying his shoe, the truck rolled out of gear. I yelled at him. He looked up just as the truck was on top of him. He dropped their food and jumped out of the way. The truck went right over the leftovers, smashed it flat. Then it crashed into another car. I looked, but the ghost was gone. Then Edith yelled something at me, and I turned and ran. I don't know if she recognized me or not.

I'm sure no one here is interested in reading another regurgitation of what a rot or skin changer is. What I'm going to concentrate on is a disturbing trend I see among some hunters, specifically in how they look at monsters.

I think a common and possibly fatal mistake is to assume that monsters are of human origin. I've heard skin changers referred to as humans who can turn into animals. How do we know that the reverse isn't the case? Maybe skin changers are animals that can disguise themselves as humans in order to better hunt us. Perhaps as civilization progressed, they piggybacked along, learning technology and learning how to better hide among us. This points out the serious flaw in assuming that there is something "salvageable" in monsters. We don't even know if they are human, never mind if they can truly feel emotions or if they can see humans as anything other than food. I've only heard of skin changers taking the form of predators, like wolves. Those are meat-eaters. Killers.

As I stated before, I've taken steps to cut all ties to my former life and am "laying low" to avoid attracting attention. Trust me, when you have money and power, you get attention. When you seem to have nothing, no one notices you.

When you live this way, you gain a new perspective on life, not unlike the horrific one we've all gained. For example, most of the good sleeping spots are taken in bad weather. If you want something, you have to fight for it. So when the rain hit, I wasn't surprised to find my spot under the bridge occupied. What was odd was the bum who evicted me. Most of the homeless wallow in misery on their best days, unless they're stoned or drunk. This one seemed oddly exuberant. He offered to share the spot and his food, and joked with the people huddled under the shelter.

Perhaps my natural suspicion of any goodwill, no matter your station in life, got the better of me. I looked at him. That was the first time I saw a monster out during daylight.

There was something wrong about him, but I couldn't put my finger on it. It was as if living under a bridge and getting by on

scraps was normal for this guy, as if the homeless people were intruding on his turf, rather than the other way around.

Some of you may point to this sense as evidence that not all monsters are evil. It did seem genuinely interested in the bums' condition, and it offered more comfort to them than the average person would.

Yet, I point out two things. I avoided the thing's food. I couldn't know if the food was healthy or even meant for human consumption. Furthermore, would you call a farmer fattening his livestock for slaughter a caring or concerned benefactor? The farmer's concern begins and ends with the profit his cattle provide. We must remember that we are ignorant of the ways of these creatures. Occam's razor has been broken; the simplest explanation is now officially nonexistent.

COLLUSION

Yesterday, I told my mom about how I saw a ghost try to hit Edith's boyfriend with a truck, right? So today I didn't have to work and I got mom and went by Edith's apartment. She wasn't there. I checked for her car. I did see the ghost, though. I was kind of scared, but I figured if it could really hurt people, it would have messed up that guy Edith was with instead of trying to get him with a truck. I hoped I'd be okay if I kept an eye on it.

We kind of went up and looked in the window, and it was looking right at us, so I motioned for it to come out. It looked really surprised at that, I think. (Its head is so mushed up that it's hard to see expressions, but it stood back a little, like it was startled.) It walked out to us - right through the wall! I could see stuff moving and working in what used to be its mouth, and I could see some teeth going up and down, but I couldn't hear anything. I told it I couldn't hear and it started looking around. Then it reached through mom's purse and her cell phone rang!

She answered it, and as she put it to her ear, the thing put its mouth right up near her, like its mouth was close to the phone? Mom jumped at that, but the guy motioned for her to keep listening. Mom's eyes got wide and I could hear that little sound when someone else is on the phone. She waved me over and I got as close to the phone and the ghost as I could deal with.

It wanted to know how we could see it. It asked if we were middle or something. Mom said she guessed we were, whatever that meant. Then I asked why it tried to kill that guy the other night.

It played dumb for a while, but finally said "I wasn't trying to "kill" him. I know that death doesn't solve a thing. I was just trying to scare him away." So we asked why he was doing that, and he got all weird again. So I said "Well, maybe we should talk to Edith about it" and he said "No, don't do that! She doesn't know!" "Doesn't know what?" "Doesn't know I'm still with her."

So it turns out this ghost is Ned, Edith's husband who died in a car crash. He'd driven a bunch of hours trying to get home and surprise her on their anniversary, and he fell asleep at the wheel and crashed on the highway.

So mom said that was a sad story, but did that excuse him taking it out on this other guy?

The ghost started to get mad, saying we didn't understand. As soon as he said that, I winced. I mean, when you talk with my mom that's like walking into a trap. I almost beat her to it, but she got out "Why don't you explain it to me?"

What he said was that, as long as Edith remembered him, it made it easier for him to hang around. If she forgot him, he thought he'd just die or something. Mom said "You don't think she's going to forget you, do you? After you got killed driving home to see her?" He said that she didn't know that either. Edith knew he'd been killed in a car crash, but she didn't know he'd worked so hard to be done early and get home. He'd tried his phone trick on her, but as soon as he said something to her, she'd get all freaked out and hang up. He really wanted to tell her about what happened, but he couldn't get through.

So we kind of offered to tell her.

ACCOMPLICE

The whole Edith/Ned thing is getting more complicated all the time. First off, there's just the normal Edith side of it. She came in to work and asked if that was me in the parking lot. Behind her is Ned, nodding his head, so I kind of admitted that, yeah, it was me. Then she asked why I ran. I shrugged, said something about being embarrassed and not wanting the hassle. She looked kind of confused. She said I probably saved her friend from an accident. Then she asked how I knew the truck was going to roll like that. I said something about how I saw it moving and remembered hearing something on the radio about trucks with bad brakes. I don't think she believed me. Adults never believe teenagers, unless you tell them something they're expecting to hear - like how stupid you are or something.

So Ned was getting agitated and started poking at the phone on the counter, but it didn't ring the way mom's phone did. Still, I picked it up. Just a dial tone, though I could see he was trying to talk to me. Edith looked at me like I was crazy, then finally thanked me and left.

Ned hung around after work, waiting for me. I couldn't hear him, but from his gestures I could see he wanted to get in the car with me, so I let him in. He started giving me directions, but when I saw he was heading for a graveyard, I went home, hoping mom would be there. She wasn't. She works a lot of nights, seeing her clients after they get off work. Lately, of course, she's been trying to follow monsters around and not get seen. She told me she's only spotted a few, but sometimes I think she's lying. Ned tried to make the phone thing work again. This time it rang and I could hear him, but it was really staticky.

He wanted me to go to the graveyard and meet some other ghosts. He said they were like him. They had leftover business and really wanted us to help them finish it. Whenever I said I wasn't sure, he got really desperate. I remember he said "Hey, why do you think you can even see us if you're not supposed to do anything?" That kind of hit home, even though he didn't know how I got into this stuff in the first place. But on the other hand, if we're "supposed" to help ghosts, wouldn't we be able to hear them, too?

Anyhow, I said there was no way I was going into a graveyard at night without my mom, and he said he understood. That was fair. Then he wanted to know how I was going to tell Edith about him. I said I didn't think it would do a lot of good to tell her if she didn't believe me, which there was no chance that she would right now.

Does anyone have any good ideas about this?

The monster was back today, and its fan club was out in force. I got closer this time, to get a better look at it and to grab some of the food it was handing out. At the very least, I might be able to figure out how to test it for poison. Does anyone know a place that tests samples? Money is no problem.

Anyway, it asked a lot of questions about the Ardus Enterprises plant that's going up on this side of town. I remember hearing about it before I went underground. Ardus was going to buy up a few blocks of decaying waterfront property and build a new waste disposal facility. Normally, you can't get a project like that to fly around here with all the liberals, but Ardus made an excellent case. They were going to target a lot of the local run down communities for employment drives, which made the liberals happy, and had plans to take on some of the city's waste management at a bargain rate, which made the conservatives happy. It was a simple but effective method to cut off opposition before it had a chance to form. No politician on either side of the line could make too much noise about the project. Considering how touchy a topic waste disposal can be with the Democrats and their tree hugging friends running things in this town, it was a move of pure genius.

To: judgmentday.list@hunter-net.org
From: serena
Subject: Re: Monsters I've Seen

> I said I didn't think it would do a lot of good to tell her if she

> didn't believe me, which

> there was no chance that she would right now.

> Does anyone have any good ideas about this?

There _are_ no good ideas about how to do it, because it's a bad idea. Look, some of these things try to ruin you directly, and some try it subtly, but _do not trust this thing_. Trust me. I'm just trying to spare you the hard knocks that I took. I listened to something that looked human, only better, and it always sounded reasonable and pitiful and it could quote the Bible and _The Merchant of Venice_ about why I should go easy on it, and when I did it killed my friend and came after me.

Put it down. That's what we're here for. If you can't do that, walk away.

To: judgmentday.list@hunter-net.org
From: thinker
Subject: Re: Monsters I've Seen

serena wrote:

>> I said I didn't think it would do a lot of good to tell her if she

>> didn't believe me, which

>> there was no chance that she would right now.

>> Does anyone have any good ideas about this?

> Put it down. That's what we're here for. If you can't do that, walk

> away.

Don't listen to Serena. If you're convinced that you can trust this Ned person and want to help him, get him to tell you some things that no one else could know about him or Edith. Every married couple has secrets like that.

Good luck on this. If you can put one of these creatures to rest without resorting to violence, I think you've done the right thing, regardless of whether it's "what the Messengers intended."

Now the plant is coming under a lot of scrutiny. There was some sort of gun battle over there. A lot of the neighborhoods that depend on the plant for work report lots of kids getting sick, even though doctors can't find anything wrong with them. So this monster's questions were pretty interesting. It asked if we'd seen any of the Ardus security guards, if they looked "funny" to us. It asked about any entrances or exits we may have seen besides the front gate, or if we knew of any people who had gone missing near the plant. The questions weren't blatant, and unless I was suspicious of him I wouldn't have thought he was trying to do anything more than make conversation.

This all ties back to my earlier message. I'm willing to bet that those monsters are messing around with the Ardus plant, maybe even poisoning those poor kids to make the company look bad. A lot of people would be out of work if the plant was closed, and the city would lose a lot of money if it had to shift waste disposers. Maybe the monsters just can't stand to see us take a small step forward. Or, if they're preying on the poor like I think they are, the extra money in the community is making their cattle a little too independent.

So the next time you see a monster treating humans as anything other than toys, remember that you don't know anything about that monster's motives. We cannot know anything of their intentions, simply because we are human and _they_ are not.

Habeas Corpus

Well, I may not need to find a way to convince Edith. Ned may be dead. Or maybe I mean "more dead." I guess he was already dead. Now maybe he's just "gone."

Mom and I went to the graveyard with him, and there were two other ghosts waiting for us, Maurice and Dorrie. Ned got mom's phone working and he was talking to us - like he was translating what the other two said? Maurice had money hidden somewhere that he wanted his son to get, and there was some complicated soap opera story about how he died protecting it. I never got to hear Dorrie's story because a bunch of what I guess were ghosts showed up. Five of them.

It was really weird. For one thing, it was like they flew in. You know the part in "The Wizard of Oz" where Dorothy's in the tornado? It was like that. It looked like their clothes and hair were flapping in the wind, but me and Mom didn't feel a thing.

Four of these new ghosts were in old-time uniforms, like in "Saving Private Ryan," and they had what looked like rifles. I couldn't see their faces, just shadows. The fifth ghost was worse. He was really skinny and naked, but with no, you know, parts. It was as if his skin was pulled really tight around his bones. He had no eyes, only dark holes. These things showed up and started fighting Ned and his friends.

The whole thing was totally weird and silent. I was screaming, trying to hit the army guys, but they just ignored me. They were holding Dorrie down and stabbing her with the knives on their rifles, leaving big cuts that didn't bleed.

Ned tried to run, but the really skinny guy was on him. The guy just touched Ned. I don't know what happened. It was like Ned just crumpled up and vanished. Like water getting sucked down a drain.

Mom ran to me in the center of them all and yelled "No!" real loud. It was like she was in the middle of an explosion. They got blasted back and tried to push in at her but couldn't. Only she'd blown Dorrie back too when that was who she was trying to save.

It was like there was a wall between us and the ghosts. At least until the skinny guy tried. He was like one of those mimes doing that "walking into the wind" thing? Only his hair was being blown back too, by whatever mom was pushing him with. But no matter how hard she pushed, he kept coming. We backed up against a wall. There was no place to go. He was almost on us. Mom was sweating and swearing and yelling real loud. That's when it spoke. "Oblivious waits for you," or something like that. We'd never been able to hear a ghost before, and we could hear this one over mom yelling and me crying.

Then everyone was gone, like they'd never been there at all. Mom and I were left standing alone against the graveyard wall.

What was that thing? I mean, I don't even know who I've become or why all this has happened to me. How am I supposed to deal with something like that?

To: judgmentday.list@hunter-net.org

From: tarjiman220

Subject: Adversaries

[I apologize for the delay in translating more information from Warden. I have been engaged in activities that I should not talk of here.]

I have followed with interest a discussion in my native language about which creature that we face is the "worst." Some say it's the apparent shape changers, because they are animals hiding among people. Others say it is the vampires that stalk the cities. A few vote for the succubi/incubi that feed on stolen emotions.

Am I the only one who sees racist undertones in this discussion? We are all very quick to say, "This type of creature does such and is evil to this degree," while, "This other type of monster behaves differently and is evil to a lesser degree." I think this kind of blanket generalization is dangerous on two levels.

I have seen what might be called vampires who are little better than homeless, standing in train stations, begging and bullying change from those who pass by. I have seen other similar creatures driven to the halls of international power by chauffeured limousines. By the same token, I have seen the [energized ones?] going about their business with no appearance of harming anyone, while others have used their powers to deceive and manipulate others for personal gain.

Which creature is most dangerous? Most likely to be well protected? Which works great ills upon humanity? I say the vampire in the expensive suit or in the position of power that associates with generals and diplomats, or the [energized one] that manipulates minds.

But it is equally possible that there are skin changers, for example, that never harm anyone. Yes, the ones who attract our attention tend to be those who rampage, but there have been a number of reports from people who see these creatures in their human forms doing nothing noteworthy. Washing windows, driving trucks, harming no one.

What am I to do in such cases? Should I scheme to release Murder, Rape and Arson so that they can fight such a seemingly innocuous creature? These criminals are proven dangerous men. Should I risk their escape to confront a creature that has only the potential to be dangerous? No. Not without a great store of information first.

So yes, you can say that I "let some go." If I see a ghost haunting drunks in the gutter, I do not concern myself with it. I have greater troubles.

Is it possible that every ghost is evil, every changer is wicked, every blood drinker is bad? Yes. I will easily accept that possibility. In the case of the vampire, it is even likely. If their need for blood conforms to folklore, it would be very hard for them to avoid harming others, simply by nature of their existence. But I believe it is necessary to look with a longer view. There are only so many creatures I can follow and observe while fulfilling my duties at the prison. I must therefore watch those creatures I feel pose the greatest threat, or that are in a position to pose the greatest threat to humanity. One does not mobilize a police force to find a solitary man who beat his wife and fled. Those officers are needed to find terrorists, drug traffickers and others whose actions harm many. Similarly, I am forced to confine my group to those creatures that are openly dangerous and who pose an immediate threat.

It has been suggested that the awakening obliges us to forget our jobs, families and stations in life in order to combat the threat. In my case, as in many I think, this is folly. If I were to turn my back on my position, I would not only arouse suspicion, I would lose resources and access that are vital to my mission. Not least of these would be my three expendable weapons.

I could leave it at that, but I will go further. I have seen a shape changer who is a police officer. I have watched him closely, as have Guard S and H. We have seen no sign of [malfeasance?] on his part. It is possible that he is not even aware of his nature.

When I think of the things Rape did before he was captured, I ask myself, what right do we humans have to condemn an entire class of beings? No, I will judge individuals by their choices and actions, not by their accidents of birth or circumstance.

That, I believe, is the heart of our existence, or at least mine. It is all well to have methods and plans for how to deal with the things out there. But if we do not know our reasons for contending with them in advance, our efforts are futile if not harmful. I must know the law as best I can before I enforce it, deciding who is an unrepentant criminal and who is not. If I don't know my own place in the judicial system, how can I be a contributor to a better society or world?

Metaphysical, perhaps, but our mission cannot be performed without some forethought and self-understanding, as with all things in life.

When we deal with other humans, we don't deal with the unknown. I'm human. I can understand the context that other people live in. I can understand how their minds work. I share a common culture with those around me. I share common traits with people around the world. I've felt love, anger, hate. I've had friends die. I've fallen in love. All those things make us human.

These monsters have felt none of that. They are utterly alien. I've seen what happens when a human "becomes" a monster. They may adopt a human seeming, but they are not human. We cannot even hope to ascribe human motivations to their actions. It is very easy to try to understand them on our terms, but we cannot. Would you say that dogs could feel love or loyalty? Of course not. A dog's "fondness" for its owner evaporates as soon as the food stops coming. We like to interpret its actions as if it was human, but it's not. It's

cute to think of a dog as faithful, to think of it as a human. It's pathetic to actually treat it like one. Monsters are the same way. We want to interpret their actions within the only context we know, the human one. But we can't afford to live and die by that.

All I can work with are the events and actions I see. The thing hiding among the homeless has shown a lot of interest in the Ardus plant. It's pumping us for information. The plant is also experiencing a lot of odd difficulties. All I can do is make a connection between them. I can't even begin to fathom why the monster is interested in the plant. All I know is that it is interested. I'm not trying to figure out what's going on in the thing's head. I can only trust what I see and draw conclusions from that.

Too many of you are far too eager to make these monsters into humans. I shudder to think that other hunters look to you for advice or guidance in these desperate times. Cut the theoretical bullshit and concentrate on what we know.

Journal Entry 4

Why do these idiots insist on projecting their wishes and desires on the monsters? I have my beliefs, but I'm not about to push them on the list. Could I live with myself if I thought my personal beliefs led someone to their death?

Many people see monsters as human, that there are those among the things that choose evil and those that choose good. They want to turn what is an obvious black-and-white situation into a vast array of confusing grays. I cannot accept this. My brother came to me as a monster. I knew him before his change, and I know that what appeared before me was not my brother. It was an impostor. His soul had already gone to its just reward.

I know I'm right. If he had to die, then they all have to die.

Born in Fire

I didn't see any fire when I got "the call." The people who say they were on fire or who saw other people covered in fire, well, it doesn't sound anything like what happened to me. I guess that's all I can say for sure.

What causes fire? It's like, friction and things changing state, right? Some people here claim to have a lot more trouble than others working their abilities, and it seemed like Ned had more trouble with his ghost-talk thing during the day. Maybe sometimes or in some places it's harder to do weird stuff? Like, there's resistance? That could be what the people's fire is here. It could be that in places with more resistance, there's more friction that causes flames. Or it could be that the fire is like the energy from those "Messengers," and in some places it's easier for the fire to come through.

I've read on the main list that some people see light or wind. Maybe it's all one thing? I mean, I remember going to a bonfire at school. It was the middle of the day and sunny, so you couldn't really see the fire, but you could feel it sucking all the air toward it. Like all the leaves and little pieces of paper? They were getting blown around by the wind from the fire. Maybe the "wind" is just fire seen in daylight, when you can't see the flames.

It could be the same thing with the light. If there is some kind of barrier between us and the Messengers, maybe when it's really thin the fire comes through so strong that it doesn't waver and it's really bright. Then you get the people with the light coming out of them. Or maybe that's when the barrier is thick and it's the increased friction that makes it steady?

Or maybe I'm full of crap. I really don't know.

CHAPTER 2: THE HUNT

*But with righteousness shall he judge the poor, and reprove with equity
for the meek of the earth: and he shall smite the earth: with the rod of his
mouth, and with the breath of his lips shall he slay the wicked.*
— Isaiah 11:4

GENERAL PRINCIPLES

To: judgmentday.list@hunter-net.org
From: tarjiman220
Subject: Heeding the Call

[Warden informs me that he has been trying to observe the main English list and is distressed by its members' apparent dissension. He has therefore asked me to deliver his ideas here only, where discussion is more considered.]

Since my change, I have spent a great deal of time considering what has become of me, or more importantly of the world as a whole. I often ask what we are supposed to do, how we are supposed to act, what our foremost concerns should be, how we should carry out our purpose. I believe that without answers to these questions, or at least theories about them, we fail to accomplish any good at all. Even the steps we take tomorrow are doomed to failure without a concept of the problems they solve.

Yet, when I turn to others out there for insight and information I fear that we are all doomed to failure. It is with great distress that I see us at each other's throats rather than at the monsters'. How long have we been awakened? The most experienced of us reports perhaps a year, if that. I have known the change for only six months. Yet already people refer to "newcomers" with scorn and criticize their naïveté. Already the scoffing cry of "you know nothing" rises from every quarter. Never mind that these self-proclaimed experts were themselves wholly ignorant of the unnatural only a few short months ago.

I had the pleasure of meeting "Professor Geo" face to face. He had come to Europe looking for the truth behind a seeming coincidence. His thoroughness is admirable.

The coincidence in question stemmed from two pieces of art: A painting of a Napoleonic-era Russian officer supposedly killed at the Battle of Leipzig, and a photograph of a notorious criminal arrested in 1865 in the United States. The Russian's name was Pyotr Rudinsky. The U.S. criminal gave his name as Peter Roads. The latter was supposedly arrested for [cannibalism?], but died in his cell before trial. A retrospective account of the case, which was the source of the photograph, claimed that Roads was captured at night and burst into flames at sunrise.

Comparing a reproduction of the painting and the photo showed an alarming similarity between the soldier and the criminal. If Professor Geo's suspicions are correct (and it is certainly a plausible explanation given what we now know of the world), this man spent at least fifty years hunting humans with relative impunity. Had he survived to the present, he would have had more experience with the supernatural than all of you and me put together.

I raise this point as an object lesson. Arrogance on the hunt is suicidal. Contention among us is unconscionable. While we squabble on the internet or in person, our collective enemy continues to gather strength as it perhaps has done for ages. If we are to succeed against any of these creatures or win even minor victories, we must focus on the true problems at hand, not on our own egos and differences of opinion.

Let that be the first lesson you learn about how we carry out our mission. You will always be rewarded by it.

A Battle of Wits

As I have said, dealing with creatures, like any reasoned activity, requires planning, thought and care. One cannot simply grab a knife and decide to battle with the unknown. As in a game of chess, one must study, advance, retreat, entice, entrap and on occasion sacrifice a pawn to take out a knight.

Let us begin with the first stage, then: scrutiny. This is vital. In a chess game, one sizes up an opponent before the game even begins, looking for signs of nervousness, uncertainty. Once the opening gambit is made, one watches for the unconscious gestures that reveal happiness or dismay.

In war and in our hunt, this observation is even more important. Watch the prey and follow it (safely, of course). Learn its habits, its residence, its needs and its strengths.

This seems an appropriate time to point out a critical weakness shared by all our so-called "prey": Their need (or desire) for secrecy. Since many readers appear to be American, I will give an example from your own history: your FBI's COINTELPRO of thirty years ago. In operations against the Ku Klux Klan, the most important part of their "hunt" was uncovering the KKK's secret membership. Once that was done, it was not difficult to frighten the Klansmen. A simple anonymous postcard reading, "We know what you are and we know what you are doing," was often sufficient to impel a member to quit the society.

As an experiment, I tried the same tactic with a creature that had recently arrived in [censored]. The very night it received the message, it fled, concealed to the eyes of all watchers. Except Guard S and H, who had the capabilities needed to pursue it outside the city.

While their bestowed abilities were up to the pursuit, their more mundane skills unfortunately were not. They lost the creature, not due to supernatural obscurity, but because he was a better driver and got past the border guards very quickly. Nonetheless, he has not returned to [censored] to our knowledge. Whatever purpose brought him there hopefully remains incomplete.

It helps, I think, to regard these creatures as if they were "secret agents." I do not belittle our situation. Creatures' greatest fear seems to be that their true face might be exposed and their true nature revealed. Since we apparently share an ability to see their true identities, their fear is a potent weapon in our arsenal.

In the future, I hope to extend this tactic into a three-stage stratagem. The first stage will frighten the creature away from its current locale or lair. In the second stage, we will follow it, perhaps rotating pursuit among myself and the guards. When a subject arrives at its destination (or if we determine that we can intercept it), an ambush will be sprung. While I would like to be able to accomplish this all with my own resources, I do not think it is feasible. It is simply too risky

To: judgmentday.list@hunter-net.org
From: shophet
Subject: Re: Conducting the Hunt

Nice advice, Warden or Tarjiman or whoever the hell you are. Too bad it cost me two close friends.

We spotted a warlock or whatever you want to call them. We'd figured out his address, and after a few days we decided to try to spook him out of his routine — so we sent him a postcard. As we were driving out to his house to see if he might've taken off _we ran into him_. Literally. He was coming the other way in a Range Rover. He must have seen us, because he swerved into our lane and drove us off the road. We rolled completely. The car came to a stop upside-down.

Crawling out, we saw him coming down the hill at us. We tried to get away, but one of my friends had a broken leg. The two of us turned to carry him when the wizard yelled something. I couldn't hear what he said too well. I guess I was deafened by the crash. But my friend, the injured one, drew his gun. With all his twisting, we lost our grip on him. I yelled at him not to shoot, but I was too late. I still don't know if it was the muzzle flash or the round itself, but either way our car exploded.

I was thrown clear, but both my friends died! I could see the warlock through the haze of the fire, shaking his head. I crawled out of there and made it back to town on foot. But I've been looking over my shoulder ever since. Here's why: I abandoned all my gear at the hotel but felt safe getting my backup bag from the bus station locker where I'd left it in on my way into town. We never even saw this warlock till we'd been here a week, so he couldn't have known about the locker.

But when I pulled out my bag, underneath was the postcard we'd sent him in the first place. Written over our message, it said, "I know where you are and I'm going to find out what you're doing."

to let my three convicts leave the prison, and extensive travel provides them greater opportunities for escape.

If a civil [quorum?] can be reached among awakened, if our lines of communication can be strengthened and, above all, if communication can be kept secure, this stratagem could be made far more efficient. For example, a hunter in Paris might discover a powerful being hides near Notre Dame. He anonymously frightens the thing away, following in secret to see where it flees. If he sees it purchase a ticket to Hamburg, he contacts a German hunter and arranges for a reception at the train station. Thus, the creature is taken unawares, away from the comfort of familiar environs and ill prepared to defend itself.

TARGETING

There are many of "them," undoubtedly more than there are of us. Simply walk out into the street at night and see which you encounter more, us or them. Any one of them is a threat to any one of us. Mark that well. Despite our capabilities, despite any possible "protection" offered by the Messengers, every one of us is human, mortal. Can you survive a bullet to the back of your head? I cannot. If a human being with nothing other than a handgun can kill you, how much more dangerous is a hundred-year-old being with the powers of darkness at its command? How much more frightening is a creature that can survive a bullet to the skull, then turn around and crush your pistol with one hand?

Every creature is dangerous. The "weak" ones are weak only in comparison to the true nightmares such as an enraged skin changer. They are all still immensely strong compared to you and me.

Thus, we fight a guerrilla war against an entrenched enemy that is superior, both in individual strength and in numbers. There is only one way to win battles in such a war. We must concentrate in numbers and strike where the enemy is spread thin.

It therefore follows, as night follows day, that we cannot strike at every creature.

I know this upsets many of you. It upsets me to see a grim specter haunting a family's home and know that I cannot run the risk of removing it, to know that the threat it poses to me and my guards outweighs the gains made from banishing it. But the logic cannot be refuted. If a patient is in critical condition, losing blood from a wound to the chest, no doctor is going to take the time to bandage a paper cut.

Therefore, when you watch a creature, you must evaluate the threat that it poses. Is it so dangerous that killing it is worth risking your life or the chance to extinguish other, more dangerous creatures?

This is not an easy decision. Many on the lists seem unable to take this long view. They live with their heads pressed to the ground, counting blades of grass when they are unable to or lack the will to see the field. Still others would demand that you follow a canonical set of guidelines, that "dead things must die first, because the living ones like warlocks are less threatening."

I cannot subscribe to such broad generalizations. I have concepts of what is right and wrong, but I judge each creature by its actions, not by its powers or its alleged nature. I believe I can respect those of you on this list enough to trust your judgment as well. (Although, in truth, I have no option. You are going to do what you wish regardless of my entreaties.) For myself, I abide by the following guidelines. The more questions to which I must answer "yes," the more compelling it is to remove the creature in question.

Is the creature frequently dangerous to the lives of people around it?

Is the creature intelligent?

Is it comparatively weak? That is, easy to kill without undue risk?

Is the creature pursuing a larger agenda? This last point is the most important to me. Even a well-protected creature that poses no immediate risk to humans is extremely dangerous if it interferes with politics, the military or other important human structures.

EXECUTION

The kill is the most important aspect of our task, the single most dangerous element (although a poor cleanup can provide almost as much risk after the fact). Once you have identified a creature, followed it, familiarized yourself with it and determined it to be dangerous enough to deserve destruction, then comes the act itself.

What can I say here that has not been said before, by those whose rosters of the dead are far longer than my own? At best, I can discuss those tactics that I know are most effective.

1) Do not work alone. The support of another person's insights and capabilities, or simply the presence of another pair of arms to strike or legs to run, is often the difference between success or failure. Get as much help as you can. Even those who have little apparent use are far from useless. They can perform minor surveillance, provide hiding places, drive you away from the scene and provide alibis if things go wrong.

2) Prepare. Like the British Boy Scouts, you must be prepared for everything. If you suspect that you are absurdly over-armed for the single creature you face, you have made a good start. I have seen a surprising number of stories online about prey who turned out to be more dangerous or more numerous than expected. I am surprised such posters have survived these missions. Why does no one ever write, "I tried to kill a creature and it was much easier than I anticipated"? I simply do not think that such [fortunate?] discoveries occur.

3) Commit. How many elaborately planned crimes have gone wrong once they are underway? The inmates of my prison are typically criminals who were indecisive. In a dangerous situation, acting on a foolish order right away is often preferable to doing nothing at all. At the very least, it gives the enemy a moving target instead of a baffled one. Hesitation is fatal. When a plan falls apart, try an auxiliary one. When that fails (which it will at some point), improvise and innovate. Perhaps you are not an expert at crisis situations? How many people truly are? A master criminal is the one who keeps his head, stays alert and behaves sensibly. The most successful soldier aims while the enemy fires nervously.

4) Know when you are beaten. This may seem ironic, after my previous advice, but a well-timed surrender can be the key to eventual triumph. I once knew of two guards who were taken hostage during a jailbreak. One fought to the end, even though outnumbered by prisoners who had guns. The other surrendered immediately, was handcuffed and used as a human shield until his captors reached a boat. They threw him into the hold and forgot about him, never remembering that he had a handcuff key of his own. He released himself, got into the engine room, overpowered the single convict there (who was not expecting trouble from their "prisoner") and sabotaged the engine.

To apply this story to our own situation: The creatures we fight appear to underestimate us. They think we are as blind as ever. They may not bother to kill us because we pose no unusual threat — at least until we play our hand. Also, many of them are said to possess mind-controlling powers that we can resist. If this is true, they might not know their mesmerism fails to affect us. They would be far more likely to drop their guard or neglect to watch us thereafter. That is your chance to escape, hopefully with some valuable information about the enemy.

EVIDENCE

Here is the most difficult, detailed and important part of our ongoing mission: concealing our presence.

I was recently angered to read, albeit loosely, a lengthy writing on the "weakness" of careful planners. A self-proclaimed "martyr to the cause" claimed that anyone who concentrated on mundane "cleanup" was a coward too concerned with his own freedom and well-being to be worthy of his role. Interestingly, this poster has not commented again in the past several weeks. I strongly suspect his cavalier attitude has landed him in prison, if not the grave. For his own sake, I hope his skills are potent protective ones.

The fact is, if you are careless, you will get caught sooner or later. Let me assure you that prison is no place for a person of intelligence and decency. Confinement with humanity's worst can make a beast of even a harmless man. Survival in jail is predicated on brutality and utter submission.

To avoid this fate, one must clean up after oneself. In less developed nations, I imagine this is less of a challenge. The police tend to lack the sophisticated databases and DNA tests of the "First World." However, since I am writing this on a computer for others with computers, I assume my audience is also at peril from technology.

Let us start with guns. American posters seem to regard these as a cure-all for any [supernatural?] problem. If one is fond of hammers, every problem begins to look like a nail. For my part, I regard every tool as a potential trap. The hand that holds the hammer cannot hold a saw, which may be more appropriate for the task presented.

Guns do damage primarily through force of impact, which sends a shock through the body. An exit wound can be large and dangerous, but many bullets pass through cleanly, leaving only small entry and exit holes. For a living man, who is an integrated system, either is enough to be fatal. But who can say with certainty if this is the case for one of the walking dead? Many report that zombies are hardly affected by bullets. A decisive blow might be best delivered with a heavy blunt or edged weapon such as an axe. Or with fire.

The primary appeal of guns is that they do their work at a distance. This is a great benefit, allowing one to harm an enemy without coming within reach of its claws or teeth. An added benefit of range, I am tempted to say the best benefit, is that it puts a psychological distance between shooter and target. Certainly standing back, aiming and pulling a trigger is less terrifying than trying to kill a creature when you are close enough to feel its breath. Close-fought battles speak to our innermost instincts. Pulling a trigger is nothing in comparison.

But the [detriment?] of reliance on guns is considerable. There is the noise, which attracts attention. There is the flash, which can pinpoint your location. A gun leaves powder burns on your hands, which can be detected by forensic science. Bullets are distinctive and can be traced. In many civilized countries, acquisition is dangerous and puts one in the debt of criminals. Furthermore, guns are not always reliable.

There are ways around these problems, to be certain. A silencer can reduce the sound (though not to the hiss you hear in films). A suppressor can reduce muzzle flash. Use of a shotgun precludes the identification of bullets. But each of these "technical fixes" introduces another layer of complexity, something else that can go wrong. Even a shotgun can be traced through the distinctive mark the hammer makes on the shell. So never eject a shotgun shell at the scene, unless you also plan to leave the weapon.

Indeed, leaving the weapon at the scene is generally a very good idea, regardless of its nature. If you have taken care to ensure that no connection exists between you and it (if you wore gloves every time you handled it, if it is not distinctive enough to be memorable, if it is not registered to you in some fashion), then leaving it behind eliminates one evidence trail cleanly at the source.

One final word on firearms: Do not believe that filing off the serial number will protect you. You will never remove it completely. My prison is full of people who thought they had completely erased such evidence.

If you are satisfied that you can safely leave a weapon at the scene, or take it away with you (with greater risk), it is time to worry about the microscopic evidence that you leave. This form of evidence is becoming increasingly important. A tiny thread or flake of dandruff can convict you.

Clothing fiber is fairly easy to account for. Wear cotton. All cotton. Any artificial fiber such as nylon or polyester can be traced to a manufacturer and sometimes to a particular clothing lot. Leave behind one thread and the police may know what color pantyhose you wore, where you bought them, when you did and possibly your size.

Your shoe print is another problem. Try to stay on stone, carpet or rocky soil. If it is going to be muddy, wear galoshes and get rid of them immediately afterward, preferably by burning them. Keep your hair and fingernails short. Wear long sleeves to avoid leaving body hair at the scene. Wear a hat.

All this assumes, of course, that you do not wish to be placed at the scene of the crime. If you plan your attack in a familiar area such as your neighborhood or workplace, you have advantage of explaining why your skin flakes and hair samples are present. However, there is a reason why convicts all over the world say, "Do not shit where you eat." Your presence makes you a suspect, and if the police can find a motive and no alibi, you may become their prime suspect.

The solution to this danger is to attack those with no connection to you. One reason "serial killers" can be so difficult to catch is that there is a vast pool of potential victims for them to choose from. One blonde prostitute, for example, is not so very different from another for their needs. There is no particular motive or connection to come to light, unlike a woman who murders her husband for insurance money or a gangster who [kills? I believe he uses a slang word here that is not in the dictionary.] a rival over a business dispute.

If you discover that your employer is a beast, confronting him yourself is doubly foolish. Reveal him to someone on the outside, someone who does not know him personally, and make sure you have a good alibi at the time of the crime. Know as little about the crime as possible, because of possible police interrogation.

One of our few advantages is that many of our targets, especially the dead ones, have no legal existence. If a person is not important, his murder will receive a cursory investigation. This is doubly true if a means of death cannot be determined, which is the case for many of our targets.

Disposing of corpses is best left to professionals. If you have killed something with a physical body, and which does not do you the courtesy of self-destructing, it is almost always better to leave it where it lies. Otherwise, you pollute your vehicle with all manner of physical evidence.

COMMITMENT

Anyone who thinks we're not in a war here needs to pull their head out of their ass.

The skin changers are animals in disguise. The demons look like walking sharks. These are signs of predators. They're not here to peacefully coexist. They're here to feed on us. They don't kill and eat us because they're afraid or because of some big misunderstanding. They're the foxes, people are the chickens and we've suddenly discovered that we're the farmer with the shotgun, only the foxes are just as quick to kill us as the chickens.

Trying to come to terms with these things is like making a deal with the devil. We have no pull here, people.

As I said earlier, unlike many of you, I've been able to give up my old life. Once I saw how the world really worked, I didn't want it anymore. I spend a lot of time on the streets now, day and night. The monsters pay little enough attention to individuals among us, so a homeless man doesn't even register with them.

Unless it's feeding time.

One of them came to the alley where I slept with a few others. I'd try to stay up all night, nursing water from a liquor bottle. I'd lay low and let the night slide by, keeping my eyes and ears open. The first night the monster came, I didn't see the bastard until it

To: judgmentday.list@hunter-net.org
From: listserver
Subject: Evidence

Attention, all hunters in the Alsace-Lorraine region. I have been in contact with several hunters in Strasbourg, Esch-sur-Alzette and Heidelberg, and they have begun a project that may help all of us avoid police attention.

It started simply enough. One of them had a gun and another needed it. After using it, the French shooter was dismissed as a suspect because he had not traveled to Germany, where the gun had been reported stolen. The Frenchman passed the gun on to a hunter in Luxembourg, who used it at a time that the previous shooter had an alibi elsewhere. Now the police are looking for someone who has traveled from Germany to France to Luxembourg. None of the people involved have been to all three countries, but their actions fool police into developing a false modus operandi for the suspect.

Reading Warden's posts, I wonder if it would be possible to create a continent-wide network of "evidence traders"? If clothes are as distinctive as he suggests, why not buy one shirt, leave a thread from it at one crime scene, then mail it to another hunter to leave as a ruse at another scene?

The downside to this prospect, of course, is that if one person is caught, the whole structure comes crashing down. That, or one captive pays the price for the crimes of the collective.

had already started to feed. Most of you report that rots look pretty normal, so maybe this one was just butt ugly. It had a big bald head and its ears were long and pointy. I'm willing to bet that's what all vampires look like, only that most of us don't have the fortitude to really see them. Not that I'm bragging. Most of the things look normal to me, too. But this one sure as hell didn't.

I let it finish. It wasn't easy, sitting there watching, but I wanted to learn more about it. Everything I had heard about bloodsuckers told me that maybe this thing wasn't one of them, or that if it was it might have different abilities. I'm all for going in with guns blazing, but ignorance will kill you faster than a dozen monsters. I might have saved that one man, but I never would have gained any information. I don't like taking people's lives into my own hands, but that's part of the job. If I couldn't deal with it, I don't think I'd be here.

When it stepped away I noticed that it was hard to see, as if the shadows were clinging to it to hide it. It didn't work. I trailed it for a while, but I had to break off when it got to a manhole cover. The thing just reached down, lifted the lid and hopped into the sewer. I almost wrecked my back when I tried to pull the cover up. There's another lesson to be learned: since these things aren't human, don't ever draw conclusions from their looks. That thing looked scrawny, but it was packing a lot more strength than my flabby ass. All that only reinforces my belief that these things aren't human in any way. Maybe they just adapt themselves to look like us.

I went to one my hiding places, stocked up on shells and waited in the alley again. It had fed well and unmolested. It would be back. I had to take it down. In retrospect, it was stupid to take the thing on alone. Remember, I was ignorant. I assumed that I knew more than I did. I'm lucky I got away with it.

I was more alert when it came back the next night, so I saw it coming. It was all inky and shadowy again, but I could see its true face.

It picked out one of the bums and started feeding. I stood up, did my best drunken stumble, and headed toward it. Now, I know these things can be distracted when feeding, but this one was absolutely surprised when I stumbled into it, jammed my shotgun into its gut and fired.

The blast knocked me on my ass. It put a big hole in the monster and a stunned look on its face, but that was about it. I panicked and started firing as fast as I could. I sprayed shot all over the alley. It was blind luck that I managed to blast enough of the thing away that it was in no shape to get me. I torched its body and got the hell out of there.

You have to get the drop on these things and you have to hit them when they're alone. We can never let the things catch us in a pattern. I know that there's a lot of advice out there, but the best I ever got was to break the rules whenever you can get away with it. That was in business, but what we do is a kind of business, too.

Before you pat me on the back, look at what I screwed up. I didn't leave any information behind for anyone else. In case you don't make it, you have to make sure someone learns what you know. Keep a journal like Doc119's and leave it where one of us will find it. We need every bit of intelligence we can gather if we want to win this war. I got lucky. The thing was obviously stupid. It was feeding alone and it was exposed. Maybe it just didn't know about people like us. We can't count on other monsters being so ignorant, especially as we step up this war. We need to strike decisively, before they identify us as a threat. I'm pretty sure there are smart monsters out there. What I saw in the business world tells me that much.

INDIVIDUAL ASSESSMENT

People on the other list and a little bit here seem to want to lump all the things we see together, because they're not us, or they're wrong or something. I can't blame my friend for the things her sister does, so I don't know how you can blame all the "monsters" we meet for the things that some of them do. That just isn't fair. I think we have to look at each of them differently. They each deserve a chance. And maybe even if all zombies or whatever are bad, maybe ghosts like Ned are okay. Who are we to judge?

Vampires

I've seen five people who drink blood in my city. That's not counting the first two, the old one and the kid, which I'm guessing were also these things.

I don't have what it takes to go after one of these guys, even if I wanted to. My mom's got the trick that lets her push things back, and even she isn't willing to get close. There are too many of them and there's just the two of us. It's too dangerous, especially when we don't know enough.

Sworn Duty

>Solomon, maybe you'd care to explain this. I've edited it for your protection, but if

>you're linked to this, I'm first in line for a piece of your ass.

>>Early Morning Gun Battle Leaves One Dead, Four Wounded

>>Police blame a gun rampage on a grudge that took a murderous turn when one homeless man

>>was killed and four others were wounded in EDITED at approximately 3 am Thursday morning, in

>>an alley near EDITED. Police spokesman EDITED told reporters, "Evidence on the scene indicates that someone

>>went into the alley and fired a shotgun repeatedly. We're combing the area

>> for evidence and are confident that the attacker knew one of the victims."

>It goes on for a bit more, but that's all we really need to see.

>Didn't anyone learn that Hannibal guy's lesson? We're here to protect people, not mow them down when they get in our way.

>Who made you judge, jury and executioner? I did.

Do you think I like the fact that I wounded those people? Do you think I wanted to do that?

When I shot that monster, I had two options. I could stand and fight it and maybe shoot my way out of there, or I could try to run. Given that I saw that thing casually lift a manhole cover, my chances of getting away from it were pretty slim.

I could turn myself in to the police, but that would be a useless gesture. There are few enough of us as it is. I made a terrible mistake that night, but the only thing I can do now is see to it that I and others never repeat them. That's my job, to lead and advise, not to give myself up.

But we watch and there are some things we've found out.

They need blood to survive, duh, but they don't always kill the people they feed off. We've watched them feed three times, and only once did the person die. The other two times we were able to make some noise or something and scare the Dracula guy away, so maybe we just interrupted them before they got done. The last one didn't seem to care that we were close. I wanted to run up and stop it, but mom wouldn't let me. I still remember the look on that poor man's face after the blood guy left.

We're watching the two living people to see if they turn into vampires, too, but so far no sign of that. We've watched one of them for three weeks now.

We think that some of these things can blank out people's minds. Now that mom knows what to look for she thinks some of her clients have been fed on before. One might get drank from regularly. Mom had him hypnotized and found out that every couple of months he drives to this house, meets someone, drives home again to sleep and forgets all about it. Whoever's brainwashing him does a good job. Mom says he's even told to eat a lot of red meat and drink plenty of liquids before and after. She can't get him to describe whoever's doing it.

At least one of these people in town also used to be human. We've seen pictures of him in the sunlight, though he never goes out in the day anymore. I don't see why turning into a vampire automatically makes you evil. It could be that it just makes you need blood to live. I mean, I guess you'd have to try really hard to not get kind of stuck-up about regular folks. Like, if you needed people, but you knew you were stronger and could hypnotize them and that you were going to live forever, I guess it would be hard to stay a good person.

But if there's anything right in movies, people don't want to become vampires. They just kind of get stuck. Some powerful thing jumps them, and suddenly they have these new powers.

Actually, that sounds kind of like us.

To: judgmentday.list@hunter-net.org

From: tarjiman220

Subject: Breeds

[I have told Warden that there is discussion here of how to contend with specific kinds of creatures and he has quickly responded with this message that has several chapters.]

I have seen discussion about the best way to harm a vampire, about whether certain plants are poisonous to skin changers, and about the usefulness of Catholic exorcism on possession victims.

I am not a soldier, doctor or priest. I am an administrator, so I have observed creatures with an eye to their organization, agendas and the possibilities of communicating with them, even if to force confessions from them.

Communication

On one level, communication with what we call vampires is simple. One merely walks up and begins a conversation. But this simplicity is a lie. Just because speaking with a vampire is physically simple does not mean it is a desirable thing to do.

Of all the things we face, vampires seem to be the most crafty and the most familiar with the ways of men. If the legends (not to mention Professor Geo's evidence) are correct, this should come as no surprise. They have had decades or centuries to observe, affect and infiltrate the governments and organizations of human kind. Given their observed powers of mind control, exerting a powerful influence on human affairs may not be a great challenge for them.

While I urge the utmost caution in communicating with these beings, I hesitate to bar such exchanges altogether. After all, while there cannot be many secrets that humanity hides from them, we are perhaps one of them.

> **To:** hunter.list@hunter-net.org
> **From:** lotus19
> **Subject:** Brussels

>I am spending more and more time in Brussels these days. I have made contact with a group of hunters who call

>themselves La Communauté Bruxe, who have made the city their personal project. Their members have decided to stay off

>the internet. If you want to contact them, reach me privately and I can try to arrange something.

>Brussels is positively thick with bloodsuckers. La Communauté is

>doing what it can, but since they're outgunned and outnumbered, they have to tread very cautiously. They're very,

>very good at observing, and they're very, very patient. If you

>want to do something about digging the rots out of the halls of power, I strongly recommend you contact them. They're

>unwilling to act decisively right now, but they'll gladly help you

>plan and execute actions against the monsters of Brussels.

>They're always happy to see someone who can act without being easily tied to the group.

>My last trip through, they got me weapons and got me out of

>town. In return, I gathered a group of European travelers (including the now-late Gerard Rosewater) and we

>bushwhacked a rot. Once we had it down, we read it the

>Communauté's list of questions before performing what Ripsaw so eloquently described as a "stake and bake."

>If it was telling the truth, NATO and the EC are both strongly influenced by vampires. He said something about a group of warlocks as well.

>He was carrying a number of documents. While the others have

>been given to the Communauté, there was one that none of us could read. I've attached a scan of it. If anyone out there can

>read it, please let me know what it says!

Accepting that we know so little about ourselves, we can reasonably hope that vampires are ignorant of our nature and purpose as well. That advantage might allow us to learn more from them than they learn from us. But before you make contact with a vampire, ask yourself if you are prepared for a battle of wits with a creature that was ancient before you were born. If you feel you are, remember that many of them can dispose of a strong man, even a hunter, as easily as you or I could break a kitten's back.

Agenda

Piqued by accounts of Brussels that I have received from a hunter called Lotus, I visited to observe. I suspect the situation is far more menacing than she believes. In a weekend, I saw no fewer than a dozen of what I believe were vampires or their blood-tainted agents. Finding them was not difficult. As Lotus indicated, many could be found near the European Community headquarters. My cursory examination revealed a slightly higher number around the headquarters of the North Atlantic Treaty Organization.

Clearly, this bears watching.

Traveler and Just Me in the U.S. both report intra-vampire conflict. Pariah Dog in the East describes something similar. It would certainly be a fine trick if we could increase this antagonism and play them one against another. However, the [detriment?] to using our enemies to do our dirty work is that they tend to work dirtier than we do. A vampire gang war is likely to leave as many humans dead as it would blood creatures, whether people are drained for "fuel" or simply caught in the crossfire. It must also be stressed that if we try to trick these beings into fighting our war for us, it is quite possible that they could trick us as well. (Perhaps that is cause for our own dissension that I addressed earlier.)

Incubi

To: judgmentday.list@hunter-net.org
From: justme
Subject: Dream ghosts?

Mom asked me to "consult" on one of her patients, which is just plain weird. She says she's gathering evidence that all kinds of creatures can mess with your brain. She thinks hypnosis is the key to fixing the things they do to people.

Anyhow, I promised not to tell too much about this patient, because of confidentiality and all. I suppose it keeps me safe too. But I have to tell you some stuff.

It was creepy because this girl was about my age. Her parents brought her in because her grades were slipping and she'd become really tired and stuff. At first they thought drugs, because, you know, they're parents and they always think it's drugs. They even got her tested, but she came up clean. She said she just wanted to sleep a lot, but it was more than that. She dropped out of band and stopped hanging out with her friends. I'll just call her Sleeper.

So mom saw Sleeper for three or four sessions, making sure she knew mom was on her side. Sleeper didn't seem like an ordinary disturbed youth or whatever. No abuse or neglect or molesting. She'd broken up with her boyfriend not long before all this happened, but she didn't seem too upset about it. "Not upset enough," was how mom said it. But still, mom didn't think there was anything strange going on until she hypnotized Sleeper.

She found out why Sleeper was so quick to, well, sleep. Almost every night, she'd dream that this gorgeous guy named Storm would come and, like, have sex with her. (This is so weird. It's weird even writing it. And I didn't make up the name Storm either.)

Mom kept asking questions and found out that these aren't like normal dreams. Storm can, you know, learn what she likes and what she doesn't and stuff. Mom even made her remember some dreams. (I'm completely glad that I didn't have to hear that part.) Mom says there's a lot of connection from one dream to the next. You know how you'll be in a play one moment, and the next you're on a bus, and then you're a baby in a stroller and it all seems normal? That kind of jumping around? Well, Sleeper's dreams don't jump around like that when she's with Storm. Other times, yeah, they're all disjointed like usual.

Here's the best part: Mom got this gadget to monitor Sleeper's heart rate. She had her wear it every night. The dreams about Storm all started about 1:30 in the morning. It didn't matter if Sleeper fell asleep early or stayed up late, the dreams were always after midnight. I don't know about you, but I used to dream even back when I could take naps during the day. (I can't do that anymore, knowing what's around out there.)

The next step was to watch her sleeping. At first mom did it at the clinic, but nothing happened. So then they went to Sleeper's house and that's when mom saw the thing.

She said it kind of "faded" into the room around one in the morning, kind of like an outline of a guy. This spirit or whatever started feeling up the girl and whispering in her ear. So mom stood up and yelled at it, which probably wasn't the smoothest move because she woke up Sleeper and her parents and got everyone kind of pissed. She gave them some line to calm them down, but the thing didn't come

back. So she wants to figure out a way to get me involved since I seem to see the weird things better than she does.

To: judgmentday.list@hunter-net.org
From: justme
Subject: More news

Well, we don't need to sneak me into mom's sessions with Sleeper. Storm has come to our house! Mom's scared. She has no idea how it followed her home. It came into her dream last night. Does anyone have any idea how to protect yourself from being followed home, or to keep yourself safe while you sleep? I mean, when we're trailing things we're really careful and all, but how do you get away from something that's not even there?

It was like, 2:00 when Mom woke me up, out of breath. She said Storm had been there and that we'd have to sleep in shifts to protect each other. It was all right out of "Nightmare on Elm Street." I asked her what happened.

At first she didn't want to talk about it much, but eventually she told me. It was really weird. She said one minute she was dreaming that she was walking through a jungle, only instead of leaves and vines, it was all chains and bottle caps. Then she came to a clearing with some kind of machine in it, like a carnival ride, and there was this guy running it. She paid him to get on and he got into the little carriage with her. She didn't say much about the ride, just that it was really slow, so they could talk. She said he was really good looking, and pretty soon she was talking to him about being divorced. She said he was laying on this line about "How lonely you must be, a single mother. You probably never have any time for your needs." Some kind of thing like that. Mom didn't go into details, but she was kind of blushing. Not like embarrassed, but like she'd just run a long way and was out of breath. Anyhow, she was on this weird ride with this guy, and she asked him his name, and he said "Storm." That's when she jerked awake.

Getting woken up in the middle of the night by my mom because some kind of demon is trying to get with her was weird enough, right? Then I got, like, this weird flash of the same symbol from this list's site. It kind of burned in my eyes the way a bulb does after you stare at it and look away. I think mom felt something too, because she said "Something's here, isn't it?" I nodded and she said "It's not Storm?" and I shook my head. Then I kind of drew the symbol on her and I drew one on myself. For some reason that helped me feel better. I fell back asleep. When I woke up in the morning, she was asleep in the chair by my bed.

I'm not sure what it all meant, but in a weird way I felt like I could finally make mom and my house safe. Maybe we all need to be able to do that.

To: judgmentday.list@hunter-net.org
From: justme
Subject: I met him

Mom asked me to take the first watch while she slept last night. She was pretty wiped from the night before, when the thing came to her. So I stayed up late watching "Rear Window" on tape. (I wanted to watch "Titanic," since it's longer and I like it better, but Mom said I probably shouldn't watch that movie when there's some kind of seducer thing around.) After the movie, I started my trig homework, which probably wasn't the smartest thing to do. One moment I was doing my math in my mom's room, the next I see this guy standing in the doorway.

Looking at him was weird. One of the guys on the big list said that when he first saw some creature it was like an optical illusion. Like one of those things where you look at it one way and it's a pretty girl, and another way it's an old woman? This was kind of like that. Part of the time he was this guy, really handsome in a cheesy sort of Hollywood way. Too perfect, with the blonde hair and this silk shirt that was open down low. But I could also see him as an ordinary guy, not so handsome, dirty-blond colored hair and this giant gash right across his throat.

I asked who he was, and he said his name was Storm. Then I asked what happened to his neck and he seemed surprised. He wanted to know how I could see that, and I said I just could. Then I asked him what he was doing in Sleeper's dream and in my mom's. That really freaked him out.

I don't know. On one hand, I thought he was some kind of evil spirit, but he really reminded more of this guy in my social studies class who I saw ask a girl out. He was kind of stupid about it, but she just shot him down and was rude and everything, and he looked like he wanted to die. Storm reminded me of that guy somehow. Like it was all an act or like I wasn't ignoring the man behind the curtain like I was supposed to.

What he wound up saying was that he gave them love, what was so wrong with that? I told him that Sleeper was getting all messed up, bad grades, dropped out of band, blah blah blah. I asked him what if some living awake-time guy asks her out and she says no because she's got Mr. Perfect in her dreams? He was getting more and more upset, said he'd leave her alone, leave us all alone, and then he got up and was heading out of the room. I got up to follow him, but I guess I was still dreaming, because when I went into the hallway, he made a gesture and the floorboards all popped up and there were these rotted hands reaching out.

I got real scared. It was like a nightmare where you really want to wake up, but you can't? I even slapped myself and nothing happened. Then all of a sudden he was next to me, the hands were gone, and he was saying it was all okay. He tried to put his arms around me, but he stopped when he saw that scared me too, and he started begging me not to be scared. It was the weirdest thing. Most of the time, when someone tries to calm you down, it's because they're worried about you, right? Storm looked really scared. Like my fear frightened him. And I guess I asked him what was going to happen, because he kept looking around like he was in trouble.

He started saying that we should both calm down, and the hallway changed. The roof sort of peeled away to this bright sunny sky. The floor turned into grass, and when I looked up the walls were gone. We were in the middle of a pasture. There was a breeze and this baby lamb was wandering around me. Only it looked kind of cartoony, more like the idea of a lamb? When I looked at Storm, he didn't have the Hollywood look. It was the other one, only he'd somehow changed clothes into turtleneck that covered up the big gash on his neck.

It sounds kind of hokey, I guess, but it was a dream. I asked him why he was so bothered that I'd get scared. He said it was complicated. Then I said "You're dead, aren't you? You're a ghost." I don't know why I hadn't thought of it before, except that I was asleep. I mean, he was just like Ned in a way, with the thing that killed him visible and everything. I guess I never thought of ghosts having sex or, like, being sexual.

Anyway, when I asked him he looked startled, but also kind of relieved. Mom told me about a couple of her patients - kids who did bad things but who were secretly relieved when they were caught. Like getting away with it scared them. I could see that kind of relief on his face. Relief that someone understood, even though it scared him.

It was weird how even though he was dead and a spirit and everything, he still really seemed to want things and act the way normal people do. I mean, I suppose I could have just freaked and gotten mom to exercize him, but he could have just come back later. This way, at least I knew what he was trying to do. Maybe some of you are going to be mad that I tried to help him, but if that helps him leave people alone, isn't it better than killing him?

He asked me how I knew about him and I told him a little bit. I didn't tell him about this list or the other one or anything. I told him about that night at the mall, that I suddenly could see things I couldn't before. Then I asked him about being a ghost. He said it sucked. Not any kind of heaven that anyone knew of, but something real close to hell. He said there were evil ghosts all around, ready to kill him. He said it's gotten a lot worse lately, too. He made it sound like ghosts think it's the end of the world.

Zombies

Communication

Judging by reports from Italy, communication with the dregs of the undead seems to be impossible. It is not a matter of language or perception. These "maldestri" (as our colleague Il_Martello terms them) simply seem to lack the capacity for rational conversation. His attempts to engage one in discourse have been met with one of two reactions. Often the zombi ignores the speaker entirely, focussing its attention elsewhere. And if greater effort is put forth by the would-be interviewer, the zombi may perceive him as a threat or impediment and attack.

Those, then, might be your conversational options with these creatures. Be ignored or (if you manage to get their attention at all) be attacked. Clearly there is little to be learned on these levels.

Agenda

Perhaps zombis' inability to communicate is limited only to us. They have been witnessed in packs, like wild dogs, so it would seem that they can recognize one of their number as a leader. Much as a charismatic politician can direct the desires of his followers, this "alpha" creature could dictate the goals of the others. Or perhaps they simply remain together out of some crude instinct or recognition and there is no leader. No "agenda" has been found for maldestri as a whole. Il_Martello believes individual packs fixate on particular people or places.

I may live to regret this statement, but there might be a straightforward means of dealing with these creatures. Unlike the "courteous wizard" described in Denmark or the skin-changing police officer I observed myself, these zombis seem to adhere to a single, mindless stereotype. There may be no ethical conflict here. They appear to be insensate beings, incapable of communication, concentration or reflection. They are focussed and dangerous. The answer, then, could be to meet them with ambush, not negotiation.

Rots

Communication

Unlike their inarticulate cousins, a swift and intelligent rot can be spoken to, if you can catch it and survive. These creatures seem to be [individuals?]. If reports out of Belize can be believed, one is more likely to see them associating with blood drinkers than with others of their own kind, though I speculate that all might be the same creature.

Whereas blood drinkers are dangerous to approach because they seem to have a natural capacity to deceive and manipulate, and zombis are dangerous because they attack if they notice you, rots neither attack nor entice. If anything, it seems that they have little interest in the living, and little to say to anyone. The exception to this might arise if you can help them accomplish a goal. If you have that to offer, they are said to become more "friendly," at least if one believes reports from someone called "Freezer."

Agenda

Rots could be extremely purposeful, but specific purpose seems to vary with the individual. The new "Dusseldorf Ripper" was reported to attack those who planned to demolish an abandoned factory. Other examples seem to indicate individual, personal vengeance. But then, who is to say what pattern might emerge from these "individual" acts if one had the perspective to recognize it?

It is interesting. There is one goal we assume every being to have: reproduction. Legends say lycanthropy and vampirism are contagious, but there is no such story about the walking dead. The mindless zombi is said to be made by a boccor or houngan in Haiti, but many of the maldestri we encounter seem to have no such master controlling them. The more intelligent walking dead have no apparent master either, nor any ability to create more like themselves. Perhaps that is why they are such "lone wolves." There simply are not enough of them to form a society.

SORCERERS

COMMUNICATION

As with vampires, communicating with sorcerers would appear to be both simple and complicated. It is simple because we do not need to perform any particular effort to achieve it. One can simply dial a telephone, if one knows the number.

As with vampires again, caution must be used. These beings are said to be powerful, rare and unpredictable. Of all the creatures we have observed, these could be most like us, for good and bad. It is good because they do not seem to need to kill or feed on us, as others do. It is bad because I know just how bad human beings can be, and I know that a little power can make a beast of even a good man. How much worse can one be with the powers sorcerers have displayed?

La Communauté Bruxe provided me the home phone number of one of the workers in the EC, with a warning to call from a public phone and to disguise my face, even though I was miles away from the sorceress. Who knows what a magician might see in her crystal ball?

I spoke briefly with the sorceress and asked what her interest was in the EC. Initially, she pretended that she was nothing more than a normal functionary. When I let her know that I had watched as she engineered a car accident that was fatal to two highly placed blood slaves, she fell silent, then suggested that we meet. I hung up immediately. I cannot explain it, but I had a strong feeling of being watched at that moment.

I am undecided whether to call her back. And if I did, what would I ask her and how much could I reveal?

AGENDA

La Communauté Bruxe has observed a number of these beings working at NATO, while a smaller number works for the EC. Note that I do not say they were seen near those places. They are employed there. In some cases, they are high-ranking officers and ministers. The very top levels seem to be purely human, but between the blood slaves and the sorcerers, both organizations are heavily compromised.

Some kind of rivalry seems to exist between the types of creatures. I have seen sorcerers eliminate both vampires and their blood slaves. I have also seen vampires pursue sorcerers with obvious dangerous intent. My first instinct in this matter is to aid the sorcerers in their battle. But can I trust my instincts in this case? The blood drinkers prey on us to survive. Do sorcerers do some harm that we simply fail to see?

The ideal would be to encourage the battle between them, but this would, I suspect, be a very difficult feat. It would mean manipulating manipulators.

While the presence of sorcerers in NATO and the EC argues loudly for some kind of master plan on their part, I could not say what it is. Vampires need our blood to live. That is their motivation for controlling us. Sorcerers? What can we possibly have that they covet?

GHOSTS

Last night Storm showed up again, although I guess his real name is Nathan. One moment I was dreaming about mowing the lawn, and then he was kind of leaning over the fence asking if he could talk to me. I said okay.

He said he wanted me to know that he wasn't going to see Sleeper any more. He'd found some old women in a retirement home and was doing the same kind of thing with them, and did I think that was wrong? He seemed kind of uncertain about it, because he was still intruding on them and everything, but on the other hand they didn't seem to mind one bit - they liked it even - and they were drugged out of their minds most of the time, anyway. I told him I guessed it was okay, as long as he didn't visit anyone too often.

Then I asked him if he knew Ned.

I'd been thinking about doing it for a while. It was like, when someone disses you and on the way home, you think of the perfect comeback? I'd been thinking "When I found out Storm was a ghost, I should have asked about Ned."

So he said "Smash Head Ned? You're the one?" I didn't like the sound of that. He said Ned had told some people - or I guess some ghosts - about meeting someone who could see him, and they were all real excited to find out who it was. Nathan says spirits want to find people who can communicate with them more than just about anything. (He called people like that "mediums," I guess because they're in the middle between the living and the dead.)

I asked him about the soldiers and that leathery thing, and he said it's an evil ghost that's been around since, like, old times. It's called Euclio and all it wants to do is destroy other ghosts. He said it's not going to your fate, like if you die and don't become a ghost. I guess Euclio stopped Ned from existing. He was just gone.

I begged Nathan not to tell anyone I was one of these mediums, and he promised. I did ask him about the other two ghosts who were with Ned - Dorrie and Maurice. He said Dorrie got vanished, eventually. I guess those soldiers we saw were Euclio's helpers. Maurice got away, but he's been hiding from them ever since.

COMMUNICATION

Communicating with the dead is problematic at best. We can see them or perhaps some of them some of the time, judging from reports of them vanishing altogether. Fewer of us report being able to hear them, and it is not clear whether they can hear us or (in extreme cases) even perceive us.

Looking through different archives, I have found multiple references to the following means of communication.

Writing. This seems by far the most common. A ghost writes something on an immaterial object and shows it to the hunter, who can perceive it.

Speech. This is (surprisingly) a seemingly rare form of communication. Ghosts do not materialize in the living world with sufficient strength to move air and communicate verbally. Or so it would seem. Perhaps those spirits who can talk prefer not to in order to conceal their abilities. Or perhaps stories of ghostly speech are tied to some mind control and our new nature makes us immune.

Technology. Some of us have reported spirits manipulating machines. They have even been said to communicate through telephones and email in some circumstances. (I find this frightening, considering the nature of our internet lists.)

Dreams. While this might appear to be a fairly safe means to communicate with the departed, there are two problems. The first is that many of us do not remember our dreams very well. For all I know, I have been holding a conversation with a ghost for months and simply do not remember it upon awakening. Second, how does one know if one has spoken to a ghost or actually dreamed it?

As I type this, a third problem comes to mind. If Freud is correct and dreams are the "royal road to the unconscious," might this mean that ghosts have the ability to plant suggestions into our minds at night, when we are most

To: judgmentday.list@hunter-net.org
From: traveler72
Subject: What are you thinking?

> I am undecided whether to call her back.

What are you thinking? If you felt like you were being watched, there's at least a chance that you were. If she hasn't tracked you down yet, maybe she missed you that time. Don't give her another chance. Use your own criteria. Is talking to her worth letting dozens of ghouls and vampires survive if she whacks you?

> And if I did, what would I ask her and how much could I reveal?

Don't tell her a goddamn thing. Don't call her, don't talk to her, don't think about her too hard. Just walk away.

Don't you realize that you may be the most organized hunter in Europe? You've got the connections in law enforcement to find things out, you're part of the system so no one will suspect you, you've got two other hunters on your side, and three psychopaths you can unleash. Don't risk all that for curiosity's sake.

To: judgmentday.list@hunter-net.org
From: thinker
Subject: Re: Sorcerers

> I am undecided whether to call her back.

Why? If her powers can find you from a brief pay phone call when you're disguised, she'll probably find you sooner or later no matter what you do.

To be safe, you probably want to use one of those voice changers. If you've got a friend in the police (or even among your inmates) who knows something about phones, he can probably reroute your call several times to make it harder to trace.

> And if I did, what would I ask her

Ask what her plans are in the government. Ask what she's doing with vampires. Ask her why we shouldn't simply shoot her from a belltower. If she says she's fighting the rots, ask her the best way to do it. She may know something we don't.

> and how much could I reveal?

About us? Don't tell her a fucking thing. If it was me, I'd play it like I was a vampire lackey who got fed up playing Step 'n' Fechit for Massa Varney and is looking to switch sides.

To: judgmentday.list@hunter-net.org
From: serena
Subject: Euclio

Wait a minute. So there's this ghost out there whose whole purpose is to destroy other ghosts? How exactly is that different from what we're doing?

Look Justme, I know this "Euclio'" thing looks ugly and the other ghosts seem nice, but I think one reason we are what we are is to get them the fuck out of the mortal world. Maybe Euclio is nasty, maybe he's even evil, but the enemy of your enemy is your friend.

vulnerable? Our proposed resilience to mental influence would seem to argue against this, but such protection would also seem to keep them out entirely, which does not appear to be the case from what I piece together of the statements from "Just Me."

Agenda

It is difficult to know anything for certain about a type of being that is intangible. There may be patterns among reports, however. I have noticed multiple cases of spirits in conflict, often ones pursued by others. Il_Martello told of a rot who confided that it was "hiding" in "il mondo di vita" from powerful spirits that wished to destroy it. These spirits, it said, dwelled "beneath" our perceptions and wished to drag all souls down to them.

Is it feasible to contact these "deep" ghosts who do not enter "the world of life"? If we do so, can we make arrangements to cooperate with them in order to keep spirit troublemakers from harassing the living? And if it is feasible, is it desirable?

Shapechangers

Communication

The skin changer with whom I have the most experience (at least I suspect him to be such) maintains a normal "human" identity. Indeed, I have never seen him outside of his ordinary façade. I have seen flashes of his hidden identity (ones that he did not wittingly reveal, I believe), and he has displayed behavior that others simply have not noticed, such as labored breathing without apparent cause, body hairs that are not naturally human, and palms badly scarred as if cut as when one falls on concrete.

If it is common practice for shapeshifters to maintain human form, they may be as approachable as sorcerers and vampires. Which is to say, contact would not be physically difficult. Still, one questions the wisdom of attempting it.

Allow me recount a story from the [censored] list. Pardon the haziness of the details, but my [censored] is poor. A poster who called himself "Christian" had an ally he called "Phantom" who spent several months hunting alongside members of some sort of extended family. I am not clear on the details, but it seemed to be some sort of kinship group. (If anyone can confirm meeting "Phantom," I would be obliged, as the story may have become [confused?] or exaggerated through retelling.)

Christian's ally realized that a man he had known all his life, a traveling merchant of something or other, was a shapechanger. Since this creature had eaten at the man's table, Phantom was unwilling to simply ambush it, as he otherwise might have done.

Instead, Phantom asked about this being's nature. The man claimed to not understand. When Phantom asked him about other supernaturals, particularly vampires, the changer became agitated and told him to stay away, that he would quickly get himself into circumstances he could not handle. Phantom said that he could not simply look away as the monsters preyed on his friends and family.

They went back and forth, but before they parted they had reached an agreement. Phantom and his comrades would join up with the shapechanger in order to rid the city of a nest of particularly vile creatures.

In practice, the relationship did not work out. Yes, having the strength and viciousness of a skin changer on their side was helpful. The mere presence of the beast frightened away the blood slaves protecting the den. However, when the actual vampires came forth to defend themselves, the beast went into a murderous rage. It attacked the enemy and its fellows with equal ferocity. Phantom fled, and according to Christian, will probably never regain the full use of his arm.

If hearsay is to be believed, is communication with the skinchangers possible? Certainly. Are they desirable allies? Only to a point.

Agenda

Individual shapeshifters, like us, undoubtedly have personal goals. But is there any goal they hold in common? From the reports I have, their primary desire is to be left alone. While their brute attacks on rather than total avoidance of humans in the wilderness seem to contradict this, it makes sense if the beasts consider humans intruders on their territory. Whatever these creatures are, they are obviously predators. No predator tolerates the violation of its hunting grounds.

To: judgmentday.list@hunter-net.org
From: listserver
Subject: Ghostly alliance

Warden wrote:

> can we make arrangements to cooperate with them in order to

> keep spirit troublemakers from harassing the living? And if it is

> feasible, is it desirable?

I'm very doubtful about this. Did the Messengers imbue us to make deals with supernaturals or to keep the world safe from them? Reading Justme's story about Euclio makes me very hesitant to choose sides in this matter. Perhaps this "Nathan" is the lesser of two evils.

If you captured a Jewish pickpocket, would you send him back to Nazi Germany?

Perhaps that is all there is to werewolves. Perhaps they are beasts who want nothing more than to hunt in peace, and conflict comes solely from the intrusion of humankind.

But we must consider another alternative. Perhaps they crave privacy in the wilderness because they conceal some larger activity. Perhaps they have plans and schemes as elaborate as those of the bloodsuckers, but because they do not need human prey they are able to carry out their agenda in the forests, unseen by human eyes.

This is a disturbing possibility. Does any hunter know anyone involved in satellite observation? Many spy satellites are in the hands of NATO, are they not? Perhaps that is one reason why the sorcerers and vampires are so interested in that institution.

Others

I have put together several reports from all over the globe of sites that seem to possess what I term a "genius loci" or local spirit. Bookworm55 assures me that animistic beliefs (religions based on the idea that areas are possessed or protected by supernatural beings) are almost universal. Tarjiman has been good enough to translate some specific articles for me to discuss.

Crusader17 described "the Name Eater" in the southwestern United States, an influence that would make the residents of a town forget individuals. The individuals would then vanish, as if they had never been born.

A document called "Physician's Field Report #22" has circulated among some hunters, describing a town in which all paranormal activity was ignored by the locals, even as it occurred openly.

Crystal23 described a cliff in Canada that bled when chipped, and the nightmares that followed.

Soyboy134 reported an Australian Outback rock formation that seemed to hypnotize people and lure them to their deaths.

Is there some foundation to the notion of a local spirit?

Communication

The only person who has reported a conversation with such a thing is "Soyboy," and he learned little of value. The voice would apparently offer enticements of some kind. There was no real evidence that a spirit or animating force had any interest in an exchange of ideas. It merely seemed to lure him closer. As for Crystal, the nightmares this person had seemed intended to frighten him/her away, rather than attract. Nonetheless, there was no indication that the intelligence of the place, if any, wanted to communicate. It might have had its own agenda or purpose, or none at all.

Agenda

These areas seem to be unique. If they can communicate with each other, they must do so by means beyond our knowing. In three of four cases, they have proven [malicious?], and in the fourth case seemed simply indifferent.

If they have plans, humans may play no good part in them.

A lot of people have warned us about making deals with ghosts and stuff. But I don't think we have a lot of choice.

You remember me talking about Euclio, the really scary spirit with the dry eye holes? Well, he showed up at our house a few nights ago. Mom and me were having a pizza and watching TV when I just got this really creepy feeling. So I concentrated and he was right there, standing right in our living room, watching us. I kind of screamed and then Mom saw him too, but he held up his hands like in a "don't hurt me" way? He said he'd come in peace.

Even though I didn't want to trust him, mom said we ought to hear him out. And we could hear him, too, like at the cemetery

So he said that maybe we got off on the wrong foot. I mean, he said everything a lot fancier, so I'm putting this in my words. He said he wanted the same thing we did - to see ghosts stop bothering people. I asked him what he'd done to Ned. All he said was that there was no more Ned. We went around and around for a while, but what it came down to was that when you die, you go to this empty place. You just stop being. Either that or you get hung up in the real world and make a mess of things until you run out of steam, and then you stop existing.

He could tell I thought that was horrible and said I misunderstood, that I thought non-existence was terrible because my body had instincts to stay alive. He said that not existing is bliss, that Budists call it Nirvana, and he said something about a philosopher saying that non-being would be like a perfect sleep. He said he was just trying to put restless ghosts in their proper place.

So mom asked if being nothing is so nice, why was he still hanging around. He said he was like a "body visa" or something. He deliberately delayed his end to help others find theirs.

We were both suspicious, since he didn't seem really merciful when he sent Ned away, but he told us that if we needed him, all we had to do was ask.

Me and mom didn't talk about it, but we were both thinking about it. I didn't mention it here before. I don't know, I guess I didn't think it would do any good. No one on these lists ever agrees on anything. Anyhow, we kind of had our minds made up for us.

There was this social worker my mom knew. I'd met her a few times. I guess I can't tell you her name, but she was really nice. Anyhow, she worked at this shelter for battered women. Well, she recently fell off the balcony of her apartment and broke both her legs. Mom went to see her in the hospital and there was this cop there. He talked to my mom and asked if she knows about… damn, I guess I can't put that name in either, can I? This one guy. Mom said no. It turns out that this guy was beating his wife, and she (the wife) went to the shelter, and mom's friend - the social worker - talked her into leaving her husband. That's who the cop was asking about, the husband. Anyhow, the husband begged the wife to come back and threatened the social worker, but both of them wouldn't change their minds. So I guess he like, blew his own brains out. And the woman was really upset about it and blamed herself, but was seeing the social worker and it seemed to be going okay. But then the social worker went over the balcony. She said she was pushed. She said the guy who pushed her looked just like the dead husband.

So the social worker doesn't believe it was a ghost, and the cop is really confused. There were no signs of anyone breaking in, but no one thought the social worker was the type to do anything crazy or try to kill herself.

Mom and I suspected what was going on. We started watching and sure enough, this ghost eventually showed up at the hospital. He just walked through the wall to her room like it was completely natural. His face was fine, but it turned out that the whole back of his head was gone. There wasn't much question who or what he was.

So mom knocked him back from the social worker, who was out of it at the time. That really seemed to shake the ghost up and he ran off, like he was a coward before and being dead really hadn't changed anything. We hoped that was the end of it, but I drew that sign on the social worker and felt better about leaving her alone.

After that we checked up on the wife and her new boyfriend. We found out that her boyfriend had been killed in a car accident, so this woman was in really bad shape. Mom and I glanced at each other. We both knew who'd caused the crash. That's when I spotted the husband watching us, his head sticking out of the wall where he was hiding and spying.

I thought about what to do. Neither mom or me could hurt the guy. We could maybe just push him away or hold him in place, but not stop him. So I just kind of blurted out that this woman should come stay with mom and me, even though we only knew her through the social worker. Mom was kind of surprised. I just nodded and looked her straight in the eye, hoping she'd understand. Mom caught on pretty quick and I could tell was trying not to look around the room, even though she wanted to. The woman didn't want to come at first, but if you know my mom, she can be pretty convincing. I guess it's a part of her work.

I could tell that the husband's ghost was pretty pissed, but he didn't seem to want to jump in the car, after what we did to him at the hospital.

Later, mom and I talked about what to do. The only thing I could think of was call Euclio. We went back to the woman's house that night. We didn't even go in - just sat in the car out front. I said "Euclio" kind of quiet, like normal talking, but nothing happened. It felt dumb, but I said it louder and he appeared out of nowhere, just walking straight down the street right at us, completely naked like before. I tried to keep my eyes on his face.

He barely spoke to us. I started to tell him that I called his name. He just turned to me and said "I know" really seriously. He kind of sniffed the air after that and went straight into the house - without even opening the door. I guess I should be used to that by now.

He wasn't in there long before I saw papers and stuff flying around inside, but there was no wind or sound. When Euclio came out again, he walked up and said "Thank you for your help" and just marched down the street again.

I don't know what the guy's problem was. Maybe it wasn't such a good idea to call Euclio, but I really don't know what else we could have done. Without him, mom's friend and that woman would probably have been dead by now. We couldn't protect them forever.

I do know that I'm not going to tell Euclio about Nathan.

CHAPTER 3: HUNTER TIES

*Who shall give account to him that is ready to judge the
quick and the dead.*
— 1 Peter 4:5

ATTITUDES TOWARD ZEALOTS

[I have translated material from Warden regarding
his relations with others of our kind. He appears to have
many different theories on our natures and behavior.]

I am a little unsure what to make of the self-styled
"boia" or "revengists." On one hand, when one hears of a
disaster caused by ill-considered, headstrong attacks, it is
generally one of these warriors at the heart of it. And yet,
it is equally true that when one hears of genuine heroism
and courage that is almost madness, there too one finds a
revengist. The question then seems to be how do we best
apply their strengths while diminishing their weakness?
The answer, I think, is to realize that not every problem
yields to the simple, direct solution. It is also to realize that
some problems require only a big stick and an angry heart.

Why would anyone ever work with someone who's
always so angry and ready to hurt people?

I mean, come on. Look at the stories we've heard
right here. Ripsaw killed a little kid to get a spirit out of
her. Crusader burned a house and shot at the fire trucks
to keep them from putting it out. And what about
Warden's friends? They're murderers and rapists.

Let me tell you something that happened to me. I'm
not going to put this on the main list. Please don't anyone
repost my stuff. Traveler, I think you got me in trouble
when you reposted my stuff about Nathan and Ned.

See, one of the people on the other list decided to find
me. I've even figured out how she did it. She said she

might have seen Ned and wanted to talk to see if we were
in the same city. (For some reason she said she was a guy,
too. I don't know why.) So over email, I gave her a phone
number for a pay phone and arranged a time to talk. But
when I went to the phone, the call was really staticky and
the person was using one of those voice scramblers, like
in "Scream"? She just said "Oh, I guess we're not in the
same town," that she was in Los Angeles. "You better get
off the phone in case someone intercepted our email and
is watching for you." There wasn't much more to say.

So about a week after that, I'm coming out of work and
going to my car when this woman drives up looking really
scared. She called me by name and said my mom was in trouble.

I was kind of on my guard because she was sort of scary
looking. There was nothing I could really put my finger on.
She was just kind of nasty and not really clean, and driving
this beat up old station wagon. But she said my mom was
in trouble and she held up a file card with one of the
symbols on it. I knew she was one of us, so I got in the car.

She drove me out to the country and told me that a
vampire had spotted my mom following it, and it grabbed
her. She said she and some other hunters had been watching
the vampire too, trying to "figure out what made it tick." But
when they saw it take my mom, they realized they had to do
something right away. I asked why they'd stopped to get me
then. She said the others had surrounded the vampire's
hiding place and they'd gotten me because I'd be able to tell
if mom was under mind control or anything.

By that point I was really scared. She pulled over and said
"There it is. That's the vampire lair." It was this really old, beat

up barn in the middle of nowhere. While I was looking at it I felt this really sharp pain in my back, and I guess I passed out.

Checking myself out later, I found these two little holes in my back, all red and irritated looking. I don't know what she used on me.

I think I was out for a while before I woke up. I felt really crappy, like I couldn't wake up, even though she was slapping me. I was soaked too. I think she threw a glass of water on me trying to snap me out of it. I was tied to a chair.

She was screaming right in my face. She wasn't making a lot of sense, but I think she was yelling at me about Nathan, about how I was, like, fucking him in my dreams and how I was the Sleeper wasn't I? All this kind of crazy stuff about how she could read between the lines. "You like it, don't you?" she kept saying, talking about ghosts and stuff I guess. I kept saying "No, it wasn't me. I didn't do any of it" over and over.

I started bawling like a baby and I think that got through to her. She kind of backed off, wouldn't look at me. She asked if I was thirsty and I realized I was. I got more water all over me because I started shaking when she came near. I couldn't help it, and that got her upset again.

She started saying, "You must think I'm a horrible person," and stuff like that. Started telling me that it was for my own good. Said she'd read my posts and realized that the ghosts had gotten to me, had tricked me, that I had to be "corrected" before it was too late. I tried to tell her no, I hadn't been fooled or anything but that made her really mad. She started screaming at me about how I thought I knew everything when I didn't know anything. Yelling about how easy we are to fool and the ghosts

know all our weaknesses. She said they watch us all the time and prey on us, coming to us disguised as people we love. She really went off about "you girls" too, talking about how she remembered what it was like to be sixteen and pretty and want to get fucked by every boy you see.

While she was going off, I checked out the ropes. I was tied up good and tight, but when I looked down I saw that she'd tied my legs to the chair legs down at the ankles. All I needed to do was pull the chair legs up, and I might be able to slip the loops off. The chair was kind of rickety too. I thought I might be able to just break off the slat my wrists were tied around.

She saw me moving around and ordered me to sit still. I said I was just uncomfortable, and asked if she could loosen the ropes a little. She thought about it, but shook her head. She even looked kind of sad. She said she couldn't let me go until she could trust me. She said the ghosts had got me and that I had to be fixed so that they couldn't feed off me any more.

While she said that, she picked up this crowbar. Her lower lip was starting to quiver, and she said that when I understood, I'd be glad. I think she was about to cry, and she asked me to forgive her. I could see a shiny edge on the end of the crowbar where she'd sharpened it.

I stood up as fast as I could and jerked my legs away from the chair legs. It worked. I got up, but I was still tied to the chair and she knocked me down. I couldn't catch myself, so I fell right on my shoulder. It hurt really bad. She'd gotten mad again, and that's when something started pounding on the door.

I must have put on the clear vision at some point, because I could see everything really well. She ran over to a corner. When I got turned over she had a huge gun, and the door smashed open. She was screaming, I was scream-ing, and the guy at the door was screaming. He had an axe, but she shot him before he could hit her with it. It didn't stop him and he chopped at her hand. Blood flew every-where and she dropped the crowbar. I got one foot on the seat and managed to pull the chair apart. My hands were still behind my back, but I wasn't tied up anymore.

The guy had grabbed her and bitten her on the face, tearing off a big chunk. She shot him again. His jacket flapped as the bullets flew out his back. Then she yelled "Back!" and he flew backward like he was on strings. She dove for the crowbar, so I ran up and kicked her as hard as I could. She fell over and I stomped on her face. She rolled onto her side and passed out. Her face and hand were bleeding a lot.

It wasn't till then that I realized that the guy who saved me was that dead kid from the mall, the one Jen liked who we pulled into the car. He asked if I was all right. He was covered in blood, but he held his hands out and said "I'm not going to hurt you, okay?" I said I just wanted to get out of there, and he let me go. I took the crazy woman's car and drove out of there. I guess I left that woman with him, but I really didn't care. She was the "monster." I haven't seen her since. I probably never will.

Journal Entry 6

The mailing list is growing soft. That prison warden seems to have his head on straight. What else would you expect from someone who has to deal with criminal scum? But that teenaged girl is like a swarm of termites, slowly eating away at the cause from the inside. I can't confront her directly on the list. I'd look like a bully, and she has been through a lot. I have to admire such courage from a teenager, but it's obvious that she has to do a lot of growing up before she can truly understand how the world works. I don't want to give up on the list, since it could be a very important tool in the war, but I can't waste my time dealing with the blind.

The more I consider the problem, the more I think that Just Me may either be a dupe or one of the enemy. My suspicions were confirmed today when she attacked the most dedicated hunters I've met: the crusaders.

If we are to lead the way and make choices, then these men and women are our supporters.

It wasn't long after my encounter in the alley that I met a fellow hunter face to face for the first time. I actually met two. I've avoided speaking of them in this journal or on the internet in order to protect their privacy. I also don't want them getting mired in the softness of people like Just Me. They need to be shielded so they can keep their dedication up. After seeing them in action, I'm sure they wouldn't want it any other way.

I was positioned in an alley across the street from my old one. I was hoping that more of the monsters would show up, maybe to find out what really happened to the one I killed. Most of the street people had been scared off, though. The cops had made a token effort to track down witnesses. Maybe the monsters have some influence over law enforcement.

I first noticed the car a few nights after I fought the freak. It was parked with a view of the alley, and I could see two figures inside. I couldn't see anything strange about them, so I wrote them off as cops on a stakeout, maybe watching for anyone suspicious in the area. After the third night they spent near the alley, I decided to investigate them. Why would two cops stay around so long when all the others had given up? I found my answer as soon as I came near. Taped to the inside of the windshield was a piece of paper with one of our symbols drawn on it: — "Us" or "friends" or something.

I understood it immediately, though I don't know how. I'd seen it in daydreams before, and now seeing it in that car, a

To: judgmentday.list@hunter-net.org
From: justme
Subject: Re: Crusaders

traveler72 wrote:

> You have to look out for that vampire. He was obviously following you, and that

> means he's up to no good. I'm sorry I had any part in getting that crazy lady on your

> back. Obviously the enemy of your enemy isn't always friendly, like someone posted.

So what are you saying? That I should trust the next pissed off bitch that comes along wanting to kill everyone? That I should write off every vampire as evil? Should I hate the guy that saved my life, and like people like the woman who tried to kill me? Is that how it's supposed to be, us versus them?

You want to know how that dead kid found me? Nathan told him. So now I owe my life to a ghost and a vampire. I guess Crusader would say I'm a traitor.

I met the kid again. I'm not going to tell you his real name. Someone on here will just try to kill him. I'll just call him Vlad. That's a good vampire name, since they're "all the same," right?

He said he'd kept an eye on me after that first night. Said he felt like he owed me, like we'd saved him. Actually, he said "saved his life" and then stopped and looked really sad.

Here's what I learned from him. He'd dead and being dead sucks. Some old vampire decided he'd make a good slave, so he grabbed him out of his house, fucking killed him, and then brought him back.

I guess Vlad ran away and the old guy tried to kill him for real, and that's when me and mom and Jen came along.

I asked why he attacked Jen in the car. He said that when one of his kind gets really hungry, they lose their shit. That's why he didn't come up to me sooner. He was ashamed, and he was afraid he'd freak out around me.

But he's not a monster, he's a person. Just like you and I are, even though we can do some pretty weird stuff.

You should have heard him. He talked about how the old guy had robbed him. That was his word. He said now he'll never be able to see his parents or his sister again, because he's afraid of what he might do to them. He can't go to any kind of normal school because he can't even go outside in the day anymore. He told me how much he misses just normal sleep, like when you wake up late on a Saturday morning. He misses feeling hot and cold. He misses being able to pet a dog without it barking or running away.

So that's your "monster." Before you try to kill him or torture him, ask how you'd feel if someone tried to do that to you. Dicatrix said violence is like a drug to bad men. If you ask me, you pissed off hunters are all junkies.

tremendous sense of relief came over me. I dropped the bum act and knocked on their window. When they rolled it down, I blurted out, probably a little too quickly, "I killed that thing in the alley."

We've been the closest of allies ever since.

Adam and Eve, as I will call them, have been hunting the creatures ever since they ran into something in a parking garage. To them it's all about putting monsters down and living to see another day. Both are young, married and neither can sleep at night knowing that things are out there. Previous to our meeting, they claimed to feel directionless, flailing. They don't have to worry about that now. With the knowledge I have of the local business community's infestation, we can extract a terrible price from the monsters.

Adam is short tempered and eager to fight. I found myself unwilling to divulge to him the identities of all the monsters I had seen, simply because I suspected that he would strike out on his own to kill them. I can't afford to let him throw his life away.

Eve is similarly eager, but is more of a planner than Adam. I get the sense that her marriage is on the rocks, and that her husband might be physically abusive. She has little trouble spending nights away from home.

I've given them guidance, taken them under my wing, and shown them that we need to organize ourselves against the beasts. They're like the children I never had.

Eager allies such as Adam and Eve may favor direct confrontation too much, I admit. I feel like it's my responsibility to guide them, to see to it that their anger is focused. Without me, they're out of control, undisciplined.

ATTITUDES TOWARD THE MERCIFUL

Journal Entry 9

I have relocated to Adam's hunting lodge. "Lodge" is an exaggeration. It's more like a shack. Thank God it has indoor plumbing.

The phone line and kitchenette are added amenities. The shack is isolated, but I can keep in touch with the world and further my research with my new laptop. Distance makes it easier for me to focus on planning rather than taking a strictly local, street-level view of things (assuming the wilds don't hide their own unknown dangers). I'm also relieved that I have a home for the winter that doesn't involve a lease or anything else that leaves a paper trail.

Adam and Eve have promised to stop by once a week to drop off food and other supplies. I've spent my time scanning the internet for information related to my new calling. That was how I found my newest ally. I review the web sites of newspapers in my region, and sometimes do a search of their archives for words like "haunting," "spook" or "mutilation." The search word "cemetery" turned up a man I have dubbed Gump.

Gump is developmentally disabled. He is also nearly seven feet tall and built like a bull elephant. The article was purely a human-interest story, telling of how his physique and simple-minded nature made it difficult for him to find a job. The local cemetery had been vandalized repeatedly and Gump volunteered to look after it. A year had gone by without any problems, and the town decided to pay Gump a small salary. Not long after, several graves were "disturbed." The article didn't go into any details, but I suspect that the damage may have been related to supernatural activity.

According to some of Bookworm55's files, monsters can inhabit and control corpses. My suspicions were confirmed by Gump himself. Apparently, the trouble had ended soon after it began. When asked about it, Gump told the reporter, "It's part of my job. If I keep the cemetery nice, no one needs to wake up and complain." It was written off as an amusing comment, but the man seemed honest and frank throughout the article. To be blunt, a joke like that struck me as beyond his capacity.

I contacted Adam and Eve about my discovery. We agreed to drive out to the cemetery and speak with Gump. I was apprehensive

about the meeting. Gump could very easily compromise us. He seemed guileless from the newspaper interview, and it was not beyond the realm of possibility that he could casually mention anything we told him about the hunt to his acquaintances. But then, everything we do is fraught with dangers. Why shouldn't this be, too?

The cemetery was located in a small town. From Adam and Eve's experiences, there were few reports of monster activity outside of urban areas. My research on hunter-net confirmed that.

Gump was even more imposing in person than the article suggested. He towered above the three of us, and I had the distinct impression that he could easily have snapped my neck, had the urge struck him.

He tried to usher us away at first, explaining that no visitors were allowed after sundown. When I mentioned that we were there to talk to him about the cemetery's dead people who had been complaining, he softened up. He was still suspicious, but when we showed him the sign for ally, he immediately became more welcoming, treating us as if we were old friends. Proof positive, I think, that he is one of us.

He said, "Most people laugh when I talk about the people who live here. They think I'm making a joke. My momma told me not to try to talk too much. She said they would lock me up for being crazy. I'm not crazy. I see the people who live in the cemetery. I don't see momma, though."

I knew we had struck gold. This place was probably a breeding ground for creatures. With Adam and Eve under my direction, we could observe the area, learn what we could and then wipe out the monsters that dwelled here.

As it turned out, Gump had something to say about that.

He was giving us a tour of the cemetery when we discovered our first monster. I was keyed up and not a little bit nervous, so I was watching with this focused sight I seem to possess. We all heard a dull thudding sound. Adam, Eve and I exchanged fearful glances, yet Gump seemed unconcerned.

"Old Man Mason is back at it again," he explained with a smile.

He led us to the source of the noise, a rather elaborate monument amidst gravestones that looked relatively new. With my sight focused, I could see the wispy form of a haggard old man slamming himself into the monument. Apparently Gump could see him too, because the fool walked right up to the thing without hesitation.

"Mr. Mason, you know that your family bought you that statue. They miss you."

The spirit snarled at us; I could hear it in my head, as if the thing were speaking to my mind. Perhaps it could read our thoughts, yet Gump spoke to it aloud.

"They're wasting my fortune. I'll find them and reclaim what I earned. You're too stupid to see that," it said.

The thing looked ready to charge us. After seeing how it made a good-sized monument shake, I readied my pistol beneath my overcoat. I wasn't sure that a gun could do anything to this creature, but I wasn't going to go defenseless. I gave Adam and Eve the sign to ready their own weapons. But before we could strike, something happened that has given me more cause for second thoughts on the hunt than anything else.

Gump looked the thing in the eye and said to it "Don't call me stupid, Mr. Mason. Don't you remember that time I found your watch in the park? You lost it when they named that flower garden in your honor. Wow, your wife was so proud that day. She likes flowers."

I almost didn't believe my eyes, but the monster's rage quickly changed to sorrow. It almost looked like it was going to cry.

"You're right. I'm sorry. There's more to life than money. I should let Mary enjoy her remaining time. She'll end up like me some day. She should be happy while it lasts."

And then it disappeared.

"Does this happen with all of them?" I asked Gump.

"No. There's two mean guys who've been around here." He saw the knife and pipe that Adam and Eve held. "Can you guys help me with them?"

Since then, we've checked in with Gump every week to look after him and the cemetery. The fools around him don't realize the war he wages each and every night to keep that town from being overrun by the dead. We don't dare take any action there without Gump's approval. The chance is too great that the childlike giant will betray our secret. So far, he has remained silent. We've been careful to not let him see our car, and we take care to mention nothing of our personal lives.

But what's stuck with me is the reaction of that ghost. For a moment, it looked all too human. Are some of the monsters salvageable as the bleeding hearts on the lists insist? It's tempting to say yes. It's tempting to convince myself that some monsters can be saved, and that the war that lies ahead can be easier than it seems.

But I can't do that to myself. I have too many people counting on my guidance to wallow in false hope or sentiment. I suspect that when a monster takes the form of a human, some measure of the human consciousness remains, like when you erase a chalkboard and some of the writing lingers as faint images, visible beneath whatever is written afterward. This lingering humanity could be a weakness, but also a strength. It makes sense that something fundamentally inhuman would need some mechanism by which to manipulate or understand us. How else could they be such experts at staying hidden unless they knew us thoroughly?

We can't take the easy route out and let a few exceptions dictate our plans. Monsters are inhuman and must be destroyed. Until I see evidence of a creature's humanity that outweighs the evidence I saw in Roderick's case, I refuse to believe otherwise. Roderick's loss will not be in vain.

We've made sure to keep a careful watch over Gump, to ensure that he understands that this is a conflict. So far, he has done an admirable job of keeping his cemetery quiet. I can only hope that my trust in his abilities is not misplaced. He is too eager to speak with the beings before making a judgment, as if we should let a dangerous animal take a bite before we kill it, just to make sure that this one isn't a vegetarian.

Journal Entry 11

Today I received an unexpected Christmas gift from Gump. When we went to check up on him last night, he gave us the name and phone number of a "friend" we should contact. The slip of paper had our ally symbol on it. Gump explained that someone much like us had come to visit him. This visitor had also read the newspaper article that pointed me in Gump's direction. I called the number this morning and found myself talking to a teenager. We agreed to meet in a city park.

Journal Entry 12

The drive down to the city to meet Gump's acquaintance was worth it. I gained another follower. I'll call him Job.

He has declined to talk about his first experience for personal reasons. I can certainly understand his motives; I haven't shared much of my encounter with Roderick. I have pieced together, however, that Job was a pedestrian in traffic at the time and performed some amazing feat of strength — a capacity I define as a great asset, but which he seems to regard with shame.

Regardless, Job has since dropped out of school without his parents' knowledge. He lives off his student-loan money. I get the feeling that he doesn't expect to live long enough to worry about paying it back.

Job made more than one allusion to dying on the hunt, not by desire, but simply out of fatalism. I suppose that if any one of us allowed ourselves to consider the possibility, we'd agree. Job is not crippled by his pessimism, though. He hates the creatures and wants to destroy them. He's cut ties to his old friends. He found Gump the same way I did. He also promised to introduce me to some other people he's met.

I must admit that Job impresses me. He shows a willingness to sacrifice everything for our purpose, but I can't help but find a little showmanship in his act. He has to learn how to make an honest assessment of a situation and work from there. I'm all for making sacrifices. I went homeless for a month. But we have to decide how much of a sacrifice is necessary for each fight. Job seems all too willing to throw his life away. I'll have to watch him and make sure he takes care of himself. If we give everything in every fight, we'll get nowhere. It's important that we pace ourselves. There will be many battles and we can't afford to exhaust ourselves in anything but the final one.

Job promised to keep in touch. I'll have Adam check in with him regularly. I regret that I live too far outside the city to keep closer tabs on him.

My little brood grows. Sometimes I feel like mother duck.

Journal Entry 13

Gump is too simple to see the truth about the monsters. I can't hold him responsible for his own intellectual shortcomings. Yet, even though the man is slow he can still see what's in front of him. He deals with the "angry ones," as he calls them, strongly and decisively.

Contrast that with Marty Henderson. That's his real name. I'd reveal his address and social security number, too, if I knew them. I've taken care to protect the identities of the other hunters I've met, but Marty deserves no one's help. We're just lucky that we didn't have another Montreal on our hands when he was done. Marty is in graduate school, even though he doesn't have half of Gump's intelligence.

Eve met Marty while she was trailing a rot masquerading as Monica Sullivan. Sullivan ran a firm that competed with my own. If I remember correctly, her husband Francis had disappeared not long after she came back from a vacation in the Caribbean. I had my suspicions about foul play, since Francis' rumored mistress also disappeared at about the same time. As it turns out, Monica is dead, her body inhabited by a monster, one that most likely killed Francis

and his lover. "She" was one of the many monsters I saw entrenched in the business world after my change. It ripped me to pieces to walk away without doing something about Sullivan, but I had no idea how to dispose of her without being arrested. After I had some experience under my belt, and a group of followers, I was ready to take her down.

Marty is one of those dysfunctional science fiction enthusiasts. He had television memorabilia all over his apartment. I don't know anything about his imbuing, and I have no idea how he met the monster controlling Monica Sullivan. We thought they were lovers, because the woman slipped off to his apartment once or twice a week in the evening. Eve noticed that Henderson had one of our symbols painted on his mailbox — what she said was "hope." I decided to intervene and confront this idiot directly myself. Adam came along. I didn't want to compromise Eve. As it turned out, it wouldn't have mattered, though for Eve's sake she's lucky she didn't come along.

Maybe we were too direct. I should have stopped Adam from kicking the door open when Marty wouldn't undo the chain. I should have remembered Adam's temper but I was enraged by the idiot's claims, too.

"They're just as human as you and me," he told us. "And if you think otherwise, you're less human for it."

I'll admit that putting my gun to his face once we were inside was extreme. I let my emotions get the better of me, but the idea of this spineless coward questioning me, after all I had sacrificed and lost, was too much for me to handle. I had never let my emotions run wild before that, and I must make sure it never happens again.

I got a handle on the situation before Adam could harm the boy. I could see that cold look in Adam's eyes, and knew we had to calm down before things got ugly. We demanded to know what Henderson was doing with Monica Sullivan. His answer sickened me.

"She's just a confused, scared woman. She came back from that other place, the place where spirits are from, and just wanted

to make things even with her husband. Maybe that's a bad thing, but now she regrets it. The guilt is tearing her apart. I know she's a murderer, but locking her up isn't going to do any good. We have to figure out what's happening to her and then cure her. I'm willing to give her a second chance if it means that the others like her won't ever need one. I'm sure you want to kill her."

"We're going to kill it, buddy. It, not 'her,'" Adam answered for me. He's learned well.

"That makes you the monster. Can't you see that? They're sick and some of them want help. We're dealing with people."

He was hopeless. Could I risk everything I had accomplished so far just to reach this one deluded idiot? I realize that every one of us is important to the cause, but you have to remember that we are, as Marty put it, only human. Some of us are going to be wrong. Imagine if this fool got in touch with Gump. He'd have that poor bastard letting the monsters run roughshod over his town, as long as they said they were sorry afterward.

I tried to convince Henderson that we would leave him alone, that we didn't have any plans to destroy Sullivan. I underestimated him. He might be stupid as far as the war goes, but he knows humanity all too well. Besides, I should've known that I couldn't lie to him about something that I believed so strongly. The next day, Eve lost track of "Sullivan." It hopped a plane. It probably took Marty with it; his apartment was abandoned when we returned.

He left us a note, though. I'm not going to bother to include it here. Suffice to say that Sullivan wasn't the only monster he had been in contact with. He had given them all a description of Adam and me, and had even passed along a description of Adam's car and his license plate number. He had to warn them before we killed them, he told us in his note: "I hope this doesn't get you in trouble, but it's what I have to do."

Try telling that to Adam now that he spends every night wide awake, ready to spring for the pistol he keeps in his bedside table. I'd stay at his house, but how would we ever explain it to his wife?

If I meet another Marty Henderson, I'll pull the trigger. Adam has to live with my mistake for the rest of his life. I just hope that it's a long and happy one. Have I condemned a good man to die because of my own stupidity?

Journal Entry 14

I've passed along enough of my savings to Adam so that he can relocate. He's going to move south. The nights aren't as long down there. Something about being closer to the equator, I think. If I knew more geography, I could say for sure. I've lost a good man and it's my own fault. The enemy is amongst us. How can we ever hope to win when we can't even trust our own kind? How typically human. On the good side, Adam is still safe and I'm watching his house from a used car I bought yesterday. It looks like Marty might have scared the monsters away. If we're lucky, he painted us as so savage and bloodthirsty that none of them will tangle with us.

I've also set up a trust fund for Adam. He won't have to work fulltime, and his kids will get a college education. It's the least I could do for the man. I've put him under strict orders to stop hunting.

ATTITUDES TOWARD VISIONARIES

A disturbing trend I sense on some lists is disdain for people who watch, who plan, who search for weaknesses in the enemy's defenses. I hope that this merely indicates that the fools with short tempers are the same fools who cannot shut their mouths. Do not let someone goad you into rash action by questioning your courage. This is doubly true for someone posting on an anonymous internet forum!

Let me tell you about my experience with people who do take the long, comprehending view. The prime example to me is la Communauté Bruxe.

I will state nothing more revealing about them than I already have: their name and their obvious location. Brussels is, to paraphrase a hunter called Howitzer, "shitty with bloodsuckers." It is therefore quite necessary for la Communauté to keep a low profile. They watch and study, but do not act. By the standards of Ripsaw or Wrath, they are useless, no? But their observations have equipped me to take action in Brussels, action which I hope will turn out to be more important in the long term than any single rash butchery.

Thanks to the members of la Communauté , I knew one of the Bruxe vampires' greatest strengths: Their former control of the police mortuary. The [chief officer?] of the morgue was one of their slaves. Whenever a body came into the morgue at night, this officer would assign it a location and appoint a coroner to perform an autopsy. Of the autopsy doctors, two of them were blooded as well. These doctors were the ones who examined corpses that were bled dry. Reports were filed that made no mention of the missing blood. Indeed, these doctors were sometimes assigned to corpses that sat up, shook hands and walked away as soon as they were alone.

I suppose a walking corpse has a distinct advantage when it comes to "playing dead." According to la Communauté, these [subverted?] doctors usually brought in a change of clothes for the "dead patient." Once the creature had walked away, the doctor would replace it with another corpse, which would eventually be burned after an "inconclusive" autopsy.

Brussels' vampires apparently have the police firmly controlled and on the alert for "terrorists." The blood drinkers hunt in packs of five to six, using a variety of abilities to secure a common pool of prey. A typical pack might have one vampire of stunning beauty who acts as "bait," luring hapless people into an ambush. La Communauté has observed at least three cases in which vampires were interrupted at their tasks, either by honest police or (in two cases) by sorcerers. In all instances, the vampires fled rather than fight, heading toward crowded areas where the sorcerers (or police) would be less likely to attack.

The controlled coroners, then, were clearly the weak links in the monsters' chain of deception. I arranged a release of my three convicts and took them (along with my guards, of course) to Brussels. It went well. In all three cases, access was simple, the corrupted servants were taken unprepared, and their deaths were not noticed for some time. We had our work done in six hours. After a steak dinner, the inmates were back in their cells by midnight.

None of this success would have been possible without the revolutionary aid of la Communauté . Thanks to the group's efforts, we knew where the servants lived, when they came home, when their local postal carriers came by, and the schedules of their wives and children. We knew which ones had dogs, how many and of what type. We knew what type of security devices they had installed and we knew the deactivation codes. The dogs were put to sleep with tranquilized meat, the security systems were deactivated, the locks yielded to the attention of Arson and Rape, and the corrupt morgue attendants largely died in their beds.

Without advance intelligence, these accomplishments would have been far more difficult. I imagine I would have needed to liberate the convicts on three separate occasions, instead on a single day. Getting in would have been harder, getting out more dangerous, and the police might well have become involved.

Most importantly, the information from la Communauté revealed the enemy's weakness. Those agents were vulnerable and their removal has made hunting in Brussels far more dangerous for blood drinkers.

So that there is no doubt: I am in favor of taking the long view.

Journal Entry 16

Finally, some good news.

Job arranged a meeting with one of the people he knows. Rebecca, as I'll call her, hails from the wrong side of the tracks. From her attitude, you would have thought that I was the one from the seamy side of town. She looked me over as if I had something to prove and asked me several questions about what I was up to and how it involved her. At the time, I was somewhat annoyed by her attitude, but in retrospect I have to admire it. She is the first one who has approached me as an equal, not been intimidated by my superior knowledge or manner.

Rebecca talks a lot about her "homies." Apparently, she has strong ties to her neighborhood. The main way in which I earned her trust was by describing to her, in detail, a homeless eye view of her stomping grounds. The fact that I spent time on the street impressed her. She is concerned with keeping the things out of her neighborhood.

To: judgmentday.list@hunter-net.org
From: tarjiman220
Subject: Brussels Document

As a translator, I hoped to provide a solution to the puzzling document made available by Lotus19. The writing on the paper was no language I knew. I tried to involve Violin99, but he did not reply. I showed it surreptitiously to some translators, and it defied them as well. One suggested that it might be an antiquated Russian tribal script, perhaps a Khazar dialect.

In time, I found a historian who could translate the message, which follows. I apologize that this has taken so long. The text is difficult. If I am not wrong about what it says, it suggests the extent of the infiltration of NATO. Lotus, do you know if the creature from which you gained this was ever in Kosovo?

"Naming was true. Our [bad smelling?] friend knew. The eastern great tent* held a parent of the eastern demons. I think the eastern demon was looking for our weakness. I think the war was its forest**. If they have sent a parent, they attack. They want to conquer. I sent the cavalry fire sky. I am responsible. The parent demon died. That is worth the trouble with the eastern king."

* "Great Tent" indicates a large pavilion, what a prince might use while traveling.

** "Forest" may be a metaphor for concealment.

Currently, she leads a small group of likeminded individuals. After we spoke for a while and I earned her trust, she seemed almost relieved that someone was taking a strategic view of things.

"I don't want to have to look after anything outside of my hood. But it's good knowing that you're out there, and not just those fucking things."

While I wish she would look at this as a war, she has done a good job on her chosen battlefield. She rattled off an impressive list of things that she and her "crew" have taken down. If there are more people like her out there, choosing their ground and doing whatever it takes to keep monsters off it, this war might be won. I understand that not everyone can abandon their lives for the fight. Rebecca made it clear that she can't run away from her sons. She's lucky enough that the father is still around and she doesn't want to give him any reason to leave. It's for people like him, her sons and her grandfather that she still works two jobs to get by and fights this war.

She said, "The government's racist. They ain't gonna help us. The pigs only come around to arrest someone when they need someone to blame for crime that happens to white folks. We gotta look out for our own."

I admire her attitude. Every hunter like her helps hem the enemy in. Maybe in the future I can even drive monsters toward her, knowing that she and her allies will hunt the thing relentlessly. I don't want to needlessly risk her, but her enthusiasm and skill would go to waste if she never gets out of her neighborhood to apply them.

She told me that not all of the hunters she knows feel the same about watching over just their homes. She's going to arrange another meeting. God bless her.

BYSTANDERS

I am perpetually surprised by the contempt I hear for the unawakened, simply because they do not possess the sight or capabilities that many of us do. There is a perception that, since they lack our tricks, they must be of lesser value. It makes me wonder if the beasts and sorcerers do not feel the same about "mere humanity."

As for me, I do not look down on other people in the least, and I have personal experience on the matter. I have cultivated some friendships with law enforcement officials. (Some of them do not care what happens to criminals after sentencing. Others seem to relish stories of the degradation and suffering experienced in prison. It takes very little embellishment, often none at all, to satisfy their cravings.) One evening over brandy, I had finished a story about a rather extreme [Episode? Incident? I am not sure what word he means here.] in my prison. A prisoner was convinced that the ghosts of his victims had returned to torment him.

As I had hoped, this story sparked a series of similar ones about [Again, a difficult word. I believe it means "episodes."] in their professions. A gentleman involved in telephone and computer enforcement said he had lost one of his best agents, whom I will call Mister Y. This officer had been on the trail of a particularly relentless computer terrorist. At first, the authorities thought they were dealing with an extremely sophisticated and advanced program, since one intrusion occurred over a solid forty-eight hour period. However, the presence of pauses and typographical errors seemed to indicate a human mind, or team of them.

Eventually they completed a line trace and tracked the intrusion to a shed in the farmlands of a neighboring country. Mister Y contacted the local police and arranged for a raid, finding only one man there.

Now, the story as told by the [commissioner?] was that the man in the farmhouse was using drugs to stay awake and hack continuously, using a bucket toilet to relieve himself. When the police arrived, he attacked them in a drug-induced frenzy and managed to escape in one of their own cars, never to be recaptured.

Mister Y insisted that he had, in fact, identified the criminal as [censored], a money launderer who helped the mainland Chinese Triads gain access to the European market. The only difficulty was, said criminal was dead, beaten and dumped on the highway by the Russian mafia.

Mister Y insisted that there had to be a Russian crime connection to the business that the hacker had been assaulting, and tried to get a court order to dig up the criminal's grave. Mister Y was finally discharged after he was caught digging it up himself, unauthorized.

After this talk, l paid a visit to Mister Y and asked him about the hacker. He said the grave was empty, and that even now, forcibly retired from the police department, he continued the search. He believed he had found the man operating a questionable internet business in South America.

l agreed to pay for Mister Y's ticket on one condition: That he not confront the criminal directly, but contact me when the man was located.

This evasive suspect, as you may have concluded, was one of the walking dead. Thanks to Mister Y, Professor Geo and several of his allies eradicated him. Upon his return to Europe, l explained to Mister Y that there was more to the world than he knew. He already had his suspicions, but l would not reveal any more.

l have since turned to him for information about other criminals and their connections. Mister Y's aid has been inestimable. Perhaps he cannot identify the unnatural simply by an effort of will, but his mind is sharp and alert, which is more than can be said for many seemingly chosen for gifts. Yes, Mister Y is a defenseless person as you might define one. ls he weak? He is stronger than any of us. ls he useless? He is a professional at computer crime investigation. Do our opponents lack bank accounts? Credit cards? Investments? No power can reveal these secrets to us, but to him they are an open book.

I guess all the people who were there at the mall are bystanders, huh? Well, they don't seem to have done much about it. There haven't been any articles in the paper about monsters fighting in front of Van Maur. In fact, mom checked the little crime report section of the paper. No one said anything. As far as the people there were concerned - and there must have been, like, a dozen of them - nothing happened at all.

Actually, reading on the lists, I think there are different kinds of "bystander." (I like that word better than "pylon.") Some of us hear voices or whatever and get weird abilities. We all agree on that. But I think there are some people who are there, who see all the crap that we do, but who don't do anything. Like my friend Jen. She knew something weird and ugly happened, but she just kind of froze. Then there's the people who don't see anything wrong, and who go on not knowing just like they've not known all their lives, like all of us before.

> *Journal Entry 17*
> Happy New Year!
> I began the year as a decrepit man, 50 going on 80. Now, I've seen what the world is really about. I've gone from heading a prosperous company with a hundred employees to leading a group of a dozen odd followers in a war which we might not win in my lifetime, assuming I don't die a violent death.
> I wonder if I'll see another New Year? If I manage to, we can keep watching and prepare to strike at the most opportune times.

It's been really weird with Jen. At first, she said she didn't remember anything, but being around mom has taught me a few things about confronting your feelings. She started to get pissed off at me for no reason and accused me of getting her into trouble and stuff - at least until I started polishing my glasses. I did that once and noticed that it made her shut up. (By the way, the doctor says he thinks my eye problem might be getting better or might be operable. He wants to watch me for a while.)

Then one day after school, she broke down at my house, right in front of me and mom. She was all scared and confused by what happened, and we all started crying. We didn't tell her that mom and I had gone after stuff since, but we did say we had seen some more, and that Jen was lucky she hadn't.

I really don't want to tell her about ghosts. I don't think it would do any good to know just how many there are around. (Though I did get rid of one. Not the way you probably think, though. Nathan got me back in touch with Maurice, and I told his son where the money was. Now that his son has the money, I haven't seen or heard anything from Maurice, and Nathan says he hasn't been around, either. So maybe it's like in "Ghost," where they take care of their business and can rest after that.)

Anyhow, I drew the sign on Jen to protect her, like a lucky charm, but it doesn't really cheer her up that much. She's convinced that the monsters are going to get her now that she knows their secret. From what I've read here and on the big list, I think she's got a point.

BURDEN TO BEAR

Journal Entry 18
Adam is dead. I don't know the particulars, but it looks like he tried hunting on his own, despite my orders. I transferred some more money to the trust fund I established for him. I called his wife from a payphone and explained that I was a friend of her husband's, that I wanted to make sure she and the kids were taken care of. Smart girl. She didn't ask too many questions.

We've watched for long enough. It's time for the monsters to pay. And when I say monsters, I say blood drinkers, skin changers, spooks, shamblers, rots and whatever else is out there, by whatever name. It's also time for people like Marty Henderson to pay.

Adam died because I let a coward live. I can't allow the failures among us to make Roderick's death meaningless. I've given up far too much to stand by and let it all go to waste because some of us are too stupid to see the obvious.

From here on, you're either with me or you're dead.

CHAPTER 4: OUR FUTURE

And I saw heaven opened, and behold a white horse; and he that sat upon him was called Faithful and True, and in righteousness he doth judge and make war.
— Revelation 19:11

LONG-TERM GOALS

To: judgmentday.list@hunter-net.org
From: tarjiman220
Subject: Our Next Steps

[There has been a delay in further messages from Warden. He says he has been observing foreign lists and assembling his thoughts on our purpose across the world. I applaud his efforts and suggest that we all do the same in hopes of finding a larger answer to our common dilemma.]

I have seen that Witness1 signs his posts with "Win the Earth." But how can this be done? Some call for a general war of all "real people" against "the monsters." Can this be done? If Hitler could rouse the passions of a nation against Jews and homosexuals, how much easier would it be to create a crusade against a genuine threat?

In my more optimistic moments, I daydream about such things. But such moral crusades tend to spill over, do they not? At first, no doubt, it would be attacks on the blood drinkers and skin changers. But in my prison, I've seen many with a thirst for blood. Believe me when I tell you that a strong target's blood is rarely spilled. The most violent of men do not crave a challenge. They want a victim.

Whatever these beings we see are, they are not victims.

So when the crusade goes poorly, what happens then? Will an army of people be willing to wait upon our wisdom? I doubt it. Without easy victories, the common man has little patience for anything, let alone war, especially a war against elusive enemies who are difficult to find, and who are deadly once cornered. Realistically, an all-out war of humankind against the unknown would be 98% fruitless chasing and 2% horrifying losses.

Mankind has shown little patience with such results.

Without real threats to battle, would people simply wait? Or would they turn on their "fifth column" marshals? Awareness of blood slavery would lead to widespread suspicion. I have seen it in my prison when there are rumors of a [I believe the term is "informer"]. People turn on anyone, but they turn in particular on those they hated already. The threat of betrayal becomes a pretext for violence.

In our crusade, I am sure the Albanians would call the Serbs servants of the dead, while the Serbs would use NATO's corruption to fling the same accusation back. The Jews would accuse the Muslims, and vice versa. Black against white. Foreign against native. We have seen this before. "He is rich. He must be in league with them. Let us kill him and redistribute his wealth!" "She is successful where I failed. She must be in bed with the devils. Let us show her what a real man is like!"

I have said in the past that we must not be hasty to dismiss the unawakened, and I stand by that. But many of the same people who say "So and so has no place in the fight, he is blind" are the same ones who call for a religious war against the unknown. It is as if the individual person is worthless, and the abstract mob is infallible.

I have seen mobs. I am far more likely to trust an individual than a collective.

I think any attempt to raise an army against the beasts is futile. Possibly worse. We have seen how easily these creatures can subvert social structures, how readily they use us one against the other. Our army of revolutionaries could simply be the deciding factor between any number of would-be kings.

No, action on that scale is not called for. It is a blunt instrument and this calls for a precise one.

The main list is full of talk about big battles and attacks on creatures, but I've never seen that happening around here. Maybe my mom and I are the only hunters in town. After running into that insane woman, I'm not sure I want to meet any more.

I've seen ghosts and a few of them were dangerous and mean. But for the worst ones, we turn to Euclio. The other times, it's been more sad than scary. Mothers looking for lost children. Lovers who just don't know when to quit. Mom says that for half of them, all they need is therapy. Nathan is still around and he's a big help with the ones who don't seem to be really cruel. But there's a lot of stuff going on that I don't understand. Something between Nathan and Euclio. And those soldiers Euclio brought with him the first time don't seem to be around any more.

The vampires are a whole different matter. I've seen a few, I think, including "Vlad" and his "master." Vlad tells me that there's at least half a dozen around, mostly fighting with each other. What am I supposed to do, skip school and look for them? I don't know how to break into a house, and I wouldn't have any idea how to get past a blood slave, whatever that is.

Does anyone ever wonder if we can win against these things? I mean, sure, we can fight them and we can kill some of them. Maybe even a lot of them. But everyone keeps saying our biggest advantage is surprise. Well, if we get into a long drawn out war, it's not going to be much of a surprise, is it?

I think they'll be here forever. Most of you probably don't want to hear that, but I don't think we have what it takes to get rid of them.

I know they're reasonable, because I've talked with them. I know they're not unfeeling killers, because Vlad saved me and I'm probably a threat to him.

Maybe we can reach some kind of peace with them?

Journal Entry 22

I now have half a dozen hunters under my command. They look up to me, even after what happened to Adam. I know that I was not responsible for the events that led directly to his death, but it was my own stupidity that sent him beyond my reach. I cannot help but think of my followers as children. They need me to demonstrate how to pursue the hunt properly. Some of the more militant ones are too eager to attack without planning. We know so little about the enemy that it's critical for us to investigate their capabilities as much as possible. The information I've found on the internet is too unreliable. Most reports are contradictory, run against what little I've seen, or are too steeped in mystical babble to be of any use. On top of all that, I have no idea of many posters' intentions. The only information I can trust is the data collected by my followers. They know their lives depend on objective, intelligently compiled reports.

I'm comfortable as leader. My experience in the business world has served me well in keeping us a coherent, functioning unit. Too many hunters seem to move without proper foresight or planning. Look at Crusader17. I applaud his efforts, and he may have taken a terrible toll on the enemy, but there's no guarantee that the damage he inflicts will have any lasting impact. Do monsters have some sort of

hierarchy? If so, we must concentrate on eliminating the upper echelons, throwing the lower ranks into chaos, and cleaning up the mess that remains. We must not be blinded by body counts.

Most of the ones that we track are little more than solitary predators. So how are the monsters able to control the media and infiltrate so many bastions of power? There might be entire "strata" of monsters that we haven't dealt with yet. Maybe all we're fighting are the weak, the disposable, the bottom feeders. There could be some group that can identify the positions in society that offer them safety and security. They amass money and material goods to influence people and buy the ways and means to protect themselves.

If these creatures exist it's my job to direct the hunt against them. We can't fall into a rut of picking off targets of opportunity. That's a trap and I think that my allies would have fallen into it had I not given them direction. Adam and Eve fought the monsters as they blundered across them. The truly powerful ones probably never need to go out into public. These are the ones that we must target. But how?

I'm afraid I have no answers right now. That scares me more than any monster I've seen.

Too many among us focus on philosophizing about the hunt. I've seen mailing lists hell-bent on answering the unanswerable, chasing their own tails while the world falls apart around them. It's time for someone to step up and take a practical stance on saving us. I can only hope that there are others out there with the insight to join me on this mission.

Journal Entry 24

I feel old today.

Rebecca put me in touch with another hunter. We met, and I think I have finally found someone I can trust to lead in my place, should it ever come to that. I'll call him David. He is young, yet he possesses wisdom beyond his years. Like that movie said, "War claims youth as one of its first casualties." He was intent on hearing of my plans, and offered a lot of good advice. He agreed with my assessment of the situation and was eager to help organize an operation to discover the most powerful monsters in our area and destroy them.

David is intelligent and has a good grasp of the situation. Initially, I was jealous of him. He can alter a weapon like Eve can. What use does that make me in a fight? I can barely fire a gun. He also seems to see very clearly, like me.

It happens in the business world eventually. A hot-blooded youngster comes along to chase the old timers out of the corporate chicken roost. The hunt is no different. Yet, I can't help but feel a strong sense of satisfaction. There are others out there capable of seeing not only what must be done, but the proper way to do it. And then there are the Marty Hendersons, who deserve whatever fate worse than death I can deal them.

I will watch David for a time. If he proves worthy, I'll give him an official rank of some sort. There's no need to institute a military hierarchy, but it would be wise to designate a lieutenant. I know that the group would scatter to the wind without my guidance. If only I had a dollar for every argument I've had to end about which monster to track next or the meaning of such-and-such an event.

ULTIMATE PLAN

I have said before that a great crusade is not the way to go. I have little patience for those who tear down without offering alternatives, so I propose my "ultimate plan" for dealing with the unknown. I hope you find it more suitable than the "final solution" model.

Step One: Education and Observation

What we must do before anything else is learn what we are fighting! We do more harm than good if we simply flail around at anything that looks unnatural. I have interpreted that some posters believe vampires need blood only to harness their powers. If this is so, there could be countless "non-drinking" vampires living in peace. A blanket attack on all bloodsuckers is going to alienate those who might help us against the violent ones. Any error could be fatal, so we cannot afford a premature act.

I therefore suggest that we spend the next six months primarily in pursuit of information about the creatures. I am not saying that we should not protect the defenseless, nor that we should tolerate those who are a threat. But we must communicate what we learn with each other, we must archive our findings, and we must keep those resources secure.

Step Two: Unification and Organization

Once we know what we face, we can organize some form of coherent resistance. I hesitate to join the crowd that claims to speak for the [Heralds], but should we not consider the symbols? This may be the reason we were given them.

When a pool of information has been gathered, we can perhaps elect representatives to make policy and pick one "general" to lead us against the creatures. If we can agree to set aside our egos, fears, pride and personal agendas, we might be able to make a difference. How many have seen one creature fighting another? Their conflicts can be our victories, unless we likewise turn on ourselves. By breaking into factions and clinging to our personal grudges, we lose any chance we had for winning.

Who should "rule"? Whom shall we select as our leader? I have heard some say, "I will only follow one of the seers," or, "One who still hears the Messengers should lead." Still others say, "Only a warrior has the strength needed to lead." Me, I do not care for amazing accomplishments. Indeed, the most powerful of us are generally the most alienated. Who has heard of the "Aetherian" who can explode a creature with merely a gesture? What is the internet name of the woman who sealed the well of demons in Nellington? These people isolate themselves from us. They do not care about community, only about the hunt.

These paragons of power cannot lead us. Leadership comes not from personal might, but from the ability to reason, persuade and compromise. I will lend my support to the person who seems most reasonable and who proposes the best plan, not the one with the most kills or the most stunning capabilities.

I recommend six months of observation and intelligence gathering. After that, I propose that we give ourselves four months to get organized, to elect representatives and form a coalition. When we have a leader, a hierarchy and an agenda, we can act.

Step Three: Revelation and Eradication

Once we are organized, with leadership and communication in place, we reveal ourselves to the world. There is reason to believe that the opposition masters the media. We must provide signs that cannot be ignored. Our apparent system of communication shows that they cannot control everything.

If we drag a demon into the sun in front of a dozen people, that is a dozen more people who no longer believe their television. The more proof we can amass, the more people we can show the way.

Our first action, once an organization is in place, should be to liberate the media and cleanse it of unnatural influence. Then the information and evidence we have amassed can be presented to the people.

When that is done, the monsters' end will surely be near.

Journal Entry 27

I wish there were more on the list like Warden. His plans are sound, even if they don't go far enough. Warden's concepts cover the beginning of our calling; I've tried to complete his message. Once the public is made aware of the danger, there is still much to do. We cannot simply drag the monsters into the light and expect people to fall in behind us. I have seen the homeless feeding off a monster's scraps, and I have seen fools like Marty Henderson. Many people will side with the monsters. They're already among our ranks. Why should things be different with humanity as a whole?

Step 3: Self-Investigation

Hunters as a whole seem to be growing stronger, yet there are still those like Marty and Just Me who refrain from a decisive course of action. Before any campaign can begin, we must ensure that all in our "army" are prepared for battle. Every Marty Henderson must be dug up, dragged before his peers and made to atone for his crimes against us. Those who work for the enemy are the greatest threat to our cause. We must identify them before the final war against the monsters can begin. We must minimize our liabilities. We'll only get one chance. Once the monsters know about us, they'll make every effort to stamp us out. If we lose, we're done. We must therefore ensure that we have the best chance of winning.

Step 4: Assumption of Power

Society's leaders are only human (or so some of them must be). They can't see monsters for what they are and so can't lead effectively. They have to be replaced from among our own ranks. Only we can see the true threat. Once we've purged our own, the remainder will be fit to take power slowly. Some, like Rebecca, will wield social power, serving as important though informal community leaders. Others, who have connections to the corridors of power, must seek political office. We can start with local elections, and maybe one day influence the Senate or even the White House. We must beware of organizations such as the military or judiciary, though. They may be rife with monsters that we're unable to remove with anything short of violence.

Step 5: Revelation and Eradication

Now Warden's plan may come to a close. Once we've strengthened our ranks, and once people live under informed guidance, the time will have come to finish all monsters.

THE SCALES ARE TIPPED

I cannot tell you how disturbing it is for me to hear talk of "a war that cannot be won." Things may look grim now, especially for someone in a city with many vampires and few awakened, but where there is life, there is hope. If you think things look bad now, think how bad they were before, when there might have been none of us. How many monsters have been stopped by us that otherwise would still kill today? How many people have been saved from death or, worse, from slavery?

We did not ask to be dragged into this battle, but here we are. We cannot give up now, hang our heads and say, "It is too difficult."

Some hunters place their faith in the next world and say that the [Heralds] prove to them that a kindly God is watching over us. I cannot believe so blindly. Would benevolent creatures give such frightening power to the evil men of my prison, unless they had some secret plan? And what of the world your own ghosts describe? It is no Heaven or Hell I have heard of.

The ugly possibility is this: This world we inhabit may be all there is for us. Perhaps after death there is nothing but annihilation. Is this an argument to waste the short span of existence we are given? I think not.

The call does not charge us to withdraw, pray and meditate. We are called to fight for this world as hard as we can. If not for our own sakes, then for the sakes of those who will follow us.

EXTREMISTS

Journal Entry 28

I just re-read my plan from entry 27. I'm starting to sound like a Che Guevara or one of those other revolutionaries that were so in vogue in the '60s. I shouldn't drink before writing anything here, though I'm sure I had no more than a glass or two of wine with dinner.

Perhaps I'm just getting emotional. The strain of the past months has gone beyond anything I ever endured when I ran the business. I have to take special care to remain calm. Maybe I'll drive into the city and stroll through a museum or something, just to relax for an afternoon.

I have heard talk of madmen and [extraordinaries?] among us, but I had not met one until recently. On the pretext of a vacation with my brother, I took a trip to Luxembourg in search of the fabled "Insect." One of us, a border guard, had seen something she thought might be the creature Namh Truang described. She asked me to help her observe and evaluate.

I explained that sneaking the convicts out of the penitentiary was difficult enough without moving them across borders, and she understood. Nonetheless, she wanted something of a net around Luxembourg before confronting the creature. She hoped to alert hunters in all adjacent areas. Thus, if the Insect escaped her attack, any country it fled to would have people alert and waiting for it. Instead of giving it a chance to rest and recover, a second group might finish it where the first failed.

Her company was very encouraging, as she too felt that organization and information would be our strongest assets in our operation. Unfortunately, events intruded upon ideas.

We had located the cluster of children she suspected of comprising the creature, but closer inspection showed them to be something else altogether. They were a group of four youngsters who, to my eyes, had pale and morbid features. They might have been taken for vampires, except that they walked by daylight. Yet, I could see other signs of vitality, such as breath, pupil dilation and pulses.

As the border guard and I watched, they approached another young person. There was something different about this little boy. It was nothing monstrous or even obvious, just an odd sort of vividness. My efforts proved nothing "wrong" with him alone, but I could see a disturbance as the four others began speaking with him. His vividness seemed to be getting brighter, if that is sensible.

At that moment, we encountered the other one of our kind, except that she turned out to be wildly excessive in her actions. At first, we paid her little attention. She was just one more person in the park on a sunny Saturday. As she got closer to the children, she broke into a run. Two of the "others" looked up just as she reached them. She grabbed those two, held them close to her, looking for all the world like a mother sweeping her children into a hug. Only these children began to burn.

The two free others fled in panic, even as the border guard and I ran toward the scene. The woman dropped the two she had held and ran after the escaping pair, her adult strides quickly catching one and she seized it by the shoulder. Smoke arose from where she touched. I remember distinctly that it did not scream. Only a choked rattle arose from its open mouth until it fell to the ground and perished, its throat burned shut.

The last "other" child ran into the street and slipped down a sewer grate before my eyes. It was gone. Of the first two the woman had embraced, one was dead. The other was crawling away as quickly as it could.

I do not clearly recall what we said as we arrived on the horrid scene. She was just turning her attention on the vivid boy. The border guard stood in her path. I seized the boy and put him behind me, demanding to know what this madwoman was about.

She said, "This city is mine and I will cast out any impure beings who come here. That boy has been touched by their evil and must be cast out." The "evil" boy was

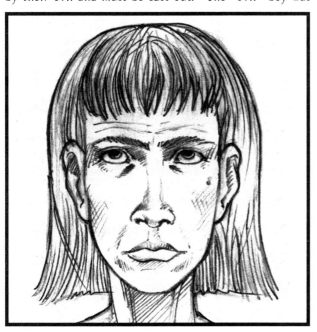

weeping and clinging to my leg, as any child might who seen his new playmates burned.

At that moment, we heard the sound of police sirens. Only then did I realize that all the people in the park had fled. The madwoman glared at us and warned that if she saw us in "her" city again, we would suffer for it. "Those who have seen and who lack the strength to fight are worse than the blind," she said before fleeing on foot.

We gave the police a full description, of course, and claimed that we thought she had flung acid on the three children. (Perhaps you have seen the newspaper stories. I have scanned in the composite sketch of the woman, which is attached to this file.)

If you see this woman, exercise great caution. She seems capable of anything.

Journal Entry 29

My museum plans had to be scrapped. The situation here took a dramatic change for the worse last night.

We have reason to believe that the local government is thoroughly corrupted by monster influence. I was discussing some of the ideas I wrote about earlier in this journal with David, about how the monsters with true power in society are not likely to be stalking homeless people in back alleys. It was David's suggestion that we investigate restaurants and social clubs where the influential and powerful gather. If the monsters have access to humans in power, wouldn't they gather at the same places? It was quite a good idea and not one that would have occurred to me.

From my experiences in the business world, the monsters had a strong grip there. It appears that their influence extends to the political sphere as well. We have not turned up evidence that any elected official is an actual monster, but we now suspect that many of them do business with creatures.

Over the past several nights, we've investigated several upscale restaurants. David also managed to get access to a country club during a large social function. He claimed that he had car trouble and needed to use their phone.

Not every place we visited harbored monsters, but there were some. I saw a rot talking to a member of the mayor's staff. The public works commissioner's top advisor is not human! Neither were the police officers hired to man that gate at the country club. These things truly are everywhere.

Lately, my encounter with the freakish vampire in the alley has received more press. The police investigation was shoddy at best. The mayor's relationship with the police union has always been strained. I understand he did not want to worsen it by laying blame on the force. Most conservative commentators wrote the incident off as more gang violence and took the opportunity to take shots at the welfare system. In other words, the shooting was largely overlooked.

Suddenly, things have changed.

Now the politicos clamor for an in-depth investigation. "Don't the homeless deserve equal protection under the law?" they ask. The police commissioner has been particularly vocal, demanding more funding in order to "nip violence like this in the bud, before it spills over into other communities."

This sudden change in the political climate takes on a sinister aspect in light of what we've seen in influential circles. Corporations have lobbyists working on their behalf. What's to stop monsters from having the same? The government might not even know it deals with monsters. Creatures or their pawns could come across as no different than environmentalists struggling to save a tree slug or as nothing more than oil company reps who want a tax break. As I learned in the business world, all it takes is a few dollars in the right pocket to get things done. What's to stop the monsters from doing the same?

Such corruption would not exist if we were in charge. We would see the monsters and eradicate their influence. Politicians can't. They're too weak to throw off monsters' influence. We must take charge if the status quo is to be broken. Society not only needs us to defend it, but to lead it. The monsters wouldn't dare eliminate us as political rivals. Imagine hunters in control of the police or city council. The death of anyone in power would attract our attention. Imagine if we could link the monsters to something like the JFK assassination! The public would finally be ready to hear about what seems like an unthinkable conspiracy.

But then, my daydreams are tempered with a note of fear. I'm worried that an investigation into events at that alley will turn up something that points in my direction. At the very least, my group's ability to operate may be severely hampered. Our activity could come under greater official scrutiny. I fully expect the police would be encouraged to react violently to any activity related to us. Imagine if the things are able to draw police protection for their lairs!

We must accept that some humans are hopelessly deluded. Until we gain control of the system, we may have to number it among our enemies. As I've said before, those who do not stand with me must be eliminated. That stands for people, not just other hunters.

I fear that our time to strike with surprise is past. The monsters are now more alert. I just pray that Marty Henderson was not somehow involved in this.

I guess I should have kept my big mouth shut, huh?

I was the one who wrote about never seeing any big attacks in my hometown. I have now.

Her name was Gina Poundstone. She was a judge of some kind, and I think she could make people see monsters, just like you and I see them.

She came into town with a group of some state troopers and two other guys in a van with that symbol I draw - the one from the web site to this list - spray painted on the side. I think the two other guys were more of us. They seemed to understand things. The police didn't quite get it all. I don't even know if they were real police. One of them said something about dressing up like that to look like they were supposed to be in charge in case of trouble. All the same, they seemed to want to be with Judge Gina for some reason.

Mom talked to the judge. She said she was going to clean out the city's vampires. I didn't hear how exactly, but mom seemed to like the idea, as if she could make it like it was before we started seeing all these things. I wondered why just vampires, but I didn't want to make trouble where there wasn't any already.

Mom told Gina about Euclio, and we called him. I wasn't sure if that was the right thing to do, but mom thought it was, so I let it go. I don't know, I think mom was secretly hoping Judge Gina would kill him. Euclio gave Gina the same line about how it just wanted to get the dead in their proper place. Gina agreed, but later - when Euclio wasn't around - she said she knew Euclio was a liar, that she didn't feel any need to keep a promise to a liar. She wanted to know if I'd try to stop her from getting Euclio when she was done with my town. I told her I guess I wouldn't. I also thought of pointing out how all we had to do was call Euclio and he'd appear, like he could hear everything we said, but I just stayed quiet. I wish I hadn't. I should have warned her - and mom.

Gina planned to make it a clean sweep, wanted to know where we'd seen vampires. Mom pulled me out of school. She figured I'd be safer with her than by myself.

I don't know what those blood people thought when we showed up at their houses, waving search warrants. I mean, the highway police sort of made sense, but then there were normal looking people – me, my mom, a judge and the two other guys. I don't even know if Gina could write search warrants. I guess it doesn't matter, because they were just distractions. They got the doors open. Sometimes the slaves fought and the police gunned them down. Sometimes the slaves just hid. Other times they surrendered. But we got to four vampires. It was so bizarre. One was in a big house right by this community center? There was a park and swimming pool and library. We dragged him out into the sun and he caught fire. The smoke drifted out over the pool where I learned to swim, and no one knew. The whole town was blind to what we were doing, like they didn't want to see.

I was terrified that we'd find Donald, but we didn't.

The last vampire jumped up off the bed as soon as we came into his room. He yelled at us, showing his fangs, and most of the police ran. The ones who stayed and the judge started shooting. Not even that killed him, but mom pushed him back while the others kept shooting. When they were done, Gina got in close to the vampire while the two other hunter guys stood there with stakes. Gina seemed to be talking to him, but I couldn't hear what she said. She just seemed real focused on him.

When she was done, she came up to me and mom and said there was another of them, a big one that was outside of town at the quarry. Gina wanted to kill it.

I didn't look at what the two guys with stakes did to that vampire guy. That's when I realized that Euclio was there. He just stood aside and watched. No one seemed to see him but me. Maybe he wanted it that way. I think he was smiling, but with that dried tight skin, he always looked like he was smiling.

I wasn't sure about going after anything outside of town. I asked Gina if she was done. She cleaned up the town like she wanted, but she said the last one had to be dealt with to finish the job. I didn't like it, but mom seemed relieved to hear that our home would be safe for once, so I didn't argue. I just wanted to make sure she'd be okay.

Gina talked to the cops that had freaked out and she seemed to calm them down. She seemed real good at that. Was I the only one who noticed?

Anyway, the cops got lamps and stuff from town. The quarry was out by the highway. Judge Gina knew right where to go. Way down at the bottom of this tunnel. Weird thing is, there was no one around, even though machines were sitting around and everything worked. When we got to the bottom we found things down there - people, a pile of dead people. Maybe they were the people who worked there or people who were driving by or hitchhikers.

I threw up. So did some of the cops.

The tunnel came to a dead end pretty quick. There was nowhere to go, so Gina told the cops to start moving bodies. She thought the big vampire might be hiding under them. I couldn't do it. I couldn't touch them. I was standing back, so I saw the mist come out of the pile. Just like this long cloud of smoke? That's when one of the cops started screaming. Then blood poured out of his mouth and eyes. It floated through the air, into the mist, and the mist was turning red.

The police guys ran. Mom tried to push it back, but she couldn't. I think she just stopped it for a while. People started shooting. It was so loud in there. I could almost see a face in the mist - eyes, teeth. Then it happened to Judge Gina. The blood poured out of her and into it.

I grabbed my mom's hand and started running. She fell down and acted like she couldn't see. That's when I realized the flashlights had gone out. I could see, but mom couldn't. She didn't know what was going on.

We left the others behind. I could hear them screaming when we got to the elevator. When the door opened, I heard a voice behind us say "He's coming." It was Euclio and he was really smiling this time. Mom must have recognized his voice, because she started screaming at him.

Euclio said something about joining him. Mom was right. We never should have trusted him. I wish I'd killed him when we first saw him at the cemetery. I dragged mom toward the elevator and hit the button inside. Euclio grabbed her other arm. It was like we were fighting over her, and the doors were closing. That's when it happened. Mom kind of looked past me, like she was searching for me in the dark. She said she loved me, then pulled herself out of my hand, and the doors closed. I pounded on the door and hit the buttons, but nothing happened. I went up.

The news had a story for everything. They said the police found out about a militia group that had explosives hidden in the quarry, where one of the militia people worked. There was an explosion or something. Gina and the other guys were never even named. Mom was never mentioned in the article, either. The newspaper claimed she was found dead at a car accident.

I don't care. I know what really happened. Who really did it all. But I don't care anymore. I let my mother die.

Now they tell me I have to go back and live with my dad and his new wife. I want to kill myself for not dying, too. This is my last post. Please unsubscribe me. I don't want to be this anymore.

Justine

DESCENT

Journal Entry 30

Just Me has finally left the list. I knew that the girl's story would end in tragedy. Ironic, isn't it, that she's driven from the hunt by a monster that she trusted? Her mother is dead and I'm sure she blames the crusading judge for it, rather than her own stupidity in dealing with the enemy.

I dare not criticize her openly. She has sacrificed a great deal for the hunt, even if it was only because of her own mistakes. I feel the pull of a new calling coming to me. There are some battles that others might not have the stomach for, yet someone must fight them. So this entry is for the one I call David in this journal. I'm going to leave you soon, but I won't abandon you without my wisdom. There is much for you and the others that will come later to learn about the hunt and our responsibility in it.

Learn from this Judge Poundstone's mistake. We cannot let our initial successes color our judgment. If you've studied history, you've seen that more conquerors have been undone by overconfidence than by a brilliant enemy. When we meet the enemy on our terms, we can win. We can't hope to win a battle fought in the enemy's stronghold when we don't know what to expect. Knowledge is power in this war. Look to the guerrilla fighters of past wars, the Viet Cong, the resistance movements of World War Two. They fought superior enemies and won. We are in a similar situation. We dare not reveal ourselves. We are surrounded by the enemy and its minions.

We cannot enter a battle unless we know exactly what we're getting into. The early stages of any war are critical. Each loss we endure now will affect us for years to come. Sometimes we'll have to be content with minor victories. Small triumphs can quickly degenerate into major defeats if we push ourselves too far. Don't get over anxious. The crusaders doubtless will be, and it's easy to convince yourself that you're unbeatable. But always remember what happened to Adam. You never met him, but I'll carry the guilt of his death to my grave. This Poundstone would have been a major asset in the war and now she's dead and useless. You must strike a careful balance between your confidence and judgment. Don't be afraid to strike, but don't be afraid to hold back, either.

An extension of this lesson is that we must nurse our resources. This is a war, not just one battle. Think two or three battles ahead until the final one. We can't risk all our resources in one conflict. Most importantly, don't be quick to risk yourself. Again, I'm guilty of this. I want to be at the front line, making a real difference. But my strength and yours is in planning, coordinating and leading. There are times when you must swallow your pride and lead from the rear. If you're a strong leader and have won the faith of your people, they won't think less of you for it. You have to put faith in the others. If you insist on looking over their shoulders all the time, micromanaging their every move, you'll quickly lose their respect. If your plan is solid and your leadership effective, you won't need to do that. Have faith in yourself, but also have faith in others.

My final advice concerns other hunters. You'll only be as effective as those who follow you. When you meet a new hunter, watch him. Do not confide in him or reveal any of your secrets. We hunters are all too human. Some are lazy. Some are incompetent. Others, such as Marty Henderson, work with the enemy against our cause. Remember what I learned from him. I don't want you to learn that lesson firsthand. It's easy to see every potential helper as a benefactor. It's a long and lonely road that lies ahead. Each person who joins our cause should make our struggle that much easier. Don't bother with those who only get in your way.

You're the leader. Remember that. At times, you'll feel the weight of the world on your shoulders. Everyone in our group will look to you for guidance and approval. You must live your life for them, not just yourself. Think of yourself as a parent leading children through a hostile world. You must care for them not only bodily, but must tend to their hearts and souls. And if you recognize someone who would do a better job of leading than you, step aside. It's all too easy to listen to your ego and convince yourself that only you are fit to lead. I debated long and hard about even letting you into my group, but I have faith in you. You're young and bold. I'm old and set in my ways, but I know enough to step down.

Good luck.

Journal Entry 31

A most unusual encounter in the park today.

I was in town checking up on Eve and the others when I had some free time to kill. I remembered my plans to go to a museum or do something to clear my head, so I decided to go out to the park.

That's where I met Thomas. A doubting Thomas.

I sat on a bench to rest for a bit. And as soon as I had taken a seat, he was there next to me.

"This is, despite all the crime at night, one of the safest places to talk about monsters," he said to me. Just like that, as if our duty was something you could chitchat about while strolling around in public.

"I've been following you for the past few weeks, trying to figure out just what it is you're up to. The way I see it, we're just as much a mystery as they are," he said.

I regained my composure long enough to make sure that he was human and that there was no one else around.

"Who are you and what do you want with me?" I asked.

"What am I would probably be a more important question, though not as important as what you are. I saw what you did to that Henderson kid. He could have been an asset to you, you know. You sure bungled that one."

I was immediately enraged. If I'd had a weapon I would have used it right then and there, to hell with the consequences.

"Look, I don't want to get involved in your little crusade, but you're starting to make more noise than you need to. If you want to start chucking nuclear bombs, you better be ready to deal with the fallout. Conflicts don't end when the last bullet's fired. Once the violence is over, things start to get really nasty."

"How do you know about me? What makes you so sure of yourself?" I was stunned that this man could accost me like this and then dare to question my decisions.

"I'll tell you this much, you haven't pulled off anything that I didn't see coming, and I've been keeping tabs on your people longer than you have. I've also seen more monsters in one night than you've seen in the past year. If you really think a 'wham, bam, thank you ma'am' war is going to solve this, you're mistaken. Step back and ask yourself why we're here. Why is this happening? You said on the list that you don't like asking those kinds of questions. Maybe that's exactly why you need to start."

He gave me a card with an e-mail address and said to keep in touch. Then he was gone. I should have followed him, but his tirade caught me flat-footed.

After a while, I came to some conclusions.

It's criminal that someone who claims to have that much information would hold it back. He's supposedly seen all these monsters, so what is he doing about it? He wasn't a monster, I could see that much, so perhaps he's one of their agents. What would have happened to me if instead of killing "Roderick" I had looked the other way and let him live? I might have even worked with him, protected him from others who would harm him.

We're too few to endure any dissension within our ranks. We stand and die together. Any who detract from our mission are working with the enemy and should be treated as such.

This task grows ever more burdensome. I can't sleep, I feel restless and I often find myself slipping into daydreams or overcome with a sudden uncontrolled rage. I smashed up the kitchen in the lodge before I sat down to write this.

What's happening? Don't I have enough troubles with the monsters?

To: [censored]
From: Solomon
Subject: Inherit the Earth!

It's important that we understand what's at stake here. Now that the war is underway, it can end in one of two ways: Either we destroy the monsters or the monsters destroy us. Once they know we're a threat, don't expect them to show us any mercy. Obviously humanity as a whole poses no threat to them. They control the government, the media, the economy. Everything. What few people hold any power are their puppets, wittingly or not.

We have tools for dealing with monsters. On the other hand, we have no special advantages when dealing with other people. My special sight shows me nothing about someone's personality. My capabilities that can affect creatures are useless against normal people. Trust me, I've tried. A cop with a gun could kill one of us. Our powers seem to be intended for use against monsters, not our fellow man. Our place is therefore at the head of humanity, leading the fight. We can't fight society, so we must direct it.

Some ask if this really has to be a war. Why must we reclaim the world from the monsters? Isn't it enough to simply punish those who take advantage of people and leave it at that?

You might remember my story of the Ardus Industries waste-disposal plant. There was a monster asking about it a while back. I never tracked that monster, though I have made an effort to look for it since. When I first encountered it I was disorganized. My resources were too limited for me to devote all of my time to a single creature. Well, it appears that I may have made a grave mistake. Two nights ago, the Ardus plant suffered what has been dubbed a "severe operational disturbance." The press hasn't provided much detail (as always seems to happen when monsters are involved), but it looks as if the plant will be out of operation indefinitely. Contacts in that area reported what sounded like an extended gun battle. The press wrote it off as gang violence, yet my reliable informant told me that was rubbish. From the sound of it, she was certain that it was a very large fight, involving several automatic weapons and perhaps even explosives. Firepower like that wouldn't be out on the streets for five minutes without her or one of her people hearing about it.

My theory is that the Ardus guards fought monstrous attackers. Obviously the monsters won, because the plant has been shut down. I have considered contacting Ardus anonymously and offering my help in tracking down the attackers, but I don't think that's feasible. No doubt Ardus has been paid off by the powers that be to stay quiet. My business experience says that if the company had truly been hurt financially, they would have made a stink about it.

What that means is the city is now paying a lot more money for waste disposal, money that could have gone to education, the elderly or the police department. A lot of people are out of work, and most of them have slim hopes of getting work with another company that paid as well as Ardus. As I wrote before, Ardus made a great effort to recruit workers from impoverished areas.

Think about that for a moment. My hometown has been damaged in countless ways by this one incident. The loss of the plant will affect the economy for years. What are the chances that any other corporation is going to move into the area after what happened here?

Situations like this demonstrate why we must take the world back from the monsters. How often have they held us back? We hear that there is enough food, water and medicine available to meet the needs of everyone on Earth, yet that doesn't happen. Water gets "polluted," "rebels" ambush convoys, "protestors" riot. How often have the monsters been behind these things? How much progress has been denied to the human race because of these things? Who's to say how many times a person has come up with a brilliant plan or invention that would advance us, only to have the monsters step in and ruin any chance of it taking root? Perhaps those crack-pot inventions they mention in the tabloids — cars that run on water, herbal cures for cancer — are actually out there, suppressed by monsters intent on keeping us down. We're cowed, brutalized and violated at their whim. The less change that occurs, the better their chance of keeping us in line.

The "progress" we've made may have been achieved only with their approval. They might assess each step we take forward, analyze how it will affect their control over us and either kill it or allow it to proceed. Think of the space program. It took us ten years to put a man on the moon. Now, thirty years later, we've gone no further. Perhaps the monsters allowed us to toy with space, but then reined us in as they considered what we could possibly achieve.

We don't fight for this world. We fight for the worlds that may have been, and for the world which could be.

Journal Entry 32

This is my final entry. David, I wish you luck. Eve, or anyone else reading this, I leave you in capable hands. Treat David with the same respect that you've shown me.

I feel younger than ever. The world is mine to change in a deep and meaningful way. Future generations will look upon us as heroes. Live up to that mantle. I've never been so proud as I am today. Months ago, I'd never have dreamed that I would feel safe leaving you to carry on the fight yourselves. I have seen you grow and I have seen you learn. I'm proud of you.

I must now prepare for a different war. There are those who would destroy you. They are worse than the monsters, because we can't see them with our gifts. The weapons we've been given won't work against them. Bullets, knives and bombs can't stop their assault. They'd corrupt your very soul and destroy your will to fight. I have appended here my last message to a mailing list that I was a part of. I have saved many of the important messages from that list on this computer. Share them with the group so that they may understand this fight, so that they may know who our true enemies are.

Do not stop fighting the monsters. That's your battle. This is mine, and you know me well enough to understand that I won't lose.

I have sent the contents of this file to the one I called Thomas. Perhaps all this will help him see the truth of our struggle and join the cause. If he doesn't, then at least he knows to fear me.

COLLAPSE

To: [censored]
From: Solomon
Subject: Last Post

This is my last e-mail to the list. I have much work to do and I have no more time to attend to the mail sent here. Most of it ends up in my trash folder, anyway.

Some of you have read Just Me's story elsewhere and undoubtedly have been swayed by her words. She has convinced you that monsters are not all monstrous, that this war cannot be won through force of arms.

It is to you that I address this message.

The ranks of my followers are growing. We track rots, blood drinkers and shamblers. If I were to give the word, we would take a terrible toll upon the creatures in our area. But I am not going to do that.

I have discovered who the enemy truly is. Over these past months, only one man under my leadership has died. He was not killed by a monster. Another hunter sent him to his fate.

We have lost track of only one monster. A hunter tipped the creature off. Who knows what crimes it has committed now that it has escaped our watchful eye.

Even as the community of hunters grows, so too does corruption within our ranks. This must stop. We are too few to allow any inner weaknesses to hinder us. This war can only end with the destruction of either the monsters or us. I intend to win, no matter what the cost.

I am leaving my followers now — they are strong enough to continue the hunt without me — because I embark on an altogether different sort of hunt.

Those who would consort with the enemy now have reason to fear the day much as the righteous fear the night.

CHAPTER 5: NEW RULES

Then hear thou from heaven, and do, and judge thy servants, by requiting the wicked, by recompensing his way upon his own head; and by justifying the righteous, by giving him according to his righteousness.
— 2 Chronicles 6:23

As a Judge, your character bears perhaps the greatest burden of all Zealots, and maybe even of all imbued. His role is not founded on personal goals or agendas, such as the Avenger's taste for revenge or the Defender's desire to protect those close to him. Although your character upholds Zeal, he does not apply it with wrath or selfishness. He must approach it impartially. For him, this Virtue is a tool brought to bear when abominations, the corrupt and wrongdoers are revealed and must be punished for their crimes against humanity. Your character is cool, calculating and expedient when higher justice must be served, and Zeal is its sword.

And yet, your character's role is not based on abundant altruism, either, such as the Innocent's compulsion to reconcile humans and creatures, or the Redeemer's hope to offer salvation. Your character decides the fate of creatures. It's not his place to reform or comfort them.

Your Judge's role is forced upon him rather than chosen or accepted. He understands monstrosities, the hunt and his place among them as an imperative, as a duty imposed through lofty concepts of Right and Wrong to which he feels obliged or beholden. Perhaps his worldview is black and white, with strictly good and bad acts and beings. Maybe he is forgiving and recognizes some actions as products of circumstance, not always personal choice.

Whether the Messengers represent or serve these higher truths doesn't matter. There is no "I choose" or "I wish" for your character, only "I must" and "I will." The Judge's role is

clear because it has to be done in the name of all things good and proper, and that has to be enough for him. What else in this twisted, foul world can your character uphold as true if not his own highest values? And if he can't swear by those ideals, how can he measure himself or others by them?

Your character's mission and sense of duty are captured in the new Traits, edges, systems and rules of this chapter. These mechanics make the arbiter's role concrete in actual play and help establish him in your unfolding chronicle. This is not to say that the following qualities and powers are exclusive to Judges. Other imbued can possess these Traits. They are simply most applicable to lawgivers and may spread among the rest of the imbued in time as Judges bring their law to the people, whether individually or to the masses.

CREATING JUDGES

Judges are often people who were decision-makers and leaders *before*. They could have been team captains, business people, organizers or parents. In normal life, they understood that there were rules that had to be obeyed or at least observed for people to get along and for life to proceed to the benefit of everyone.

These qualities may have meant that your character didn't steal or lie or cheat or betray his friends. Or perhaps they meant that he always fulfilled his responsibilities, was there when people needed him, or that he set himself as a role model for action. Ultimately, he was the person first and foremost subject to his own code of honor and ethics, and by holding himself true, he expected everyone else to fall in line. That was the right thing to do, after all.

Now that your character knows the truth about the world, his values haven't changed. In fact, they're more important than ever. If this world is going to be turned around, it has to be because the bad are set apart from the good, because the monsters are picked from the moral. Those who can't do the right thing must be identified and dealt with so that the rest may enjoy mutual respect and trust. Whether your character has ever put it into words before, he's believed in this necessity all his life. Since he's always lived this maxim, he's the best to distinguish wrong from right. Perhaps his life from before has simply led up to this moment.

New Archetypes

The following Traits may be added to your game as Natures and Demeanors.

Adjudicator

The Adjudicator is a natural and ready problem-solver. She seeks to resolve issues, differences and difficulties as a function of personality and identity, not out of any effort to achieve a specific end or to fulfill a greater goal. Her first instinct is to settle a dispute by hearing out the parties involved, or simply by offering advice or counsel. That others petition or welcome her guidance is not her concern, just that she tries to solve the problem at hand. Adjudicators can be teachers, parents, business professionals, counselors, ministers or simply busybodies.

— Regain Willpower whenever you provide a solution to a problem that results in an immediate resolution.

Stoic

The Stoic seeks to remain emotionally composed at almost all times. Problems are solved and dilemmas are faced through composure and a cool head, not with hysterics or passion. The Stoic deals strictly with the facts before him and tries not to let his own or others' emotions sway the course of action that reason and calm indicate as the most efficient, economical or effective. Military men, physicians and criminals could be Stoics.

— Regain a point of Willpower whenever you overcome a serious setback or loss without giving in to anger or other strong emotions.

Nonpartisan

The Nonpartisan deals with people and information and enters situations without preconceived notions. She measures people on what they say and do, not by their origins, appearances or mannerisms, allowing all an opportunity to show their stripes before determining how they should be dealt with. Rumor, information or intelligence is rarely taken at face value unless the source is impeccable. This is not to say that she acts without planning or cannot be impetuous, simply that she accepts few facts without testing them herself.

— Regain Willpower whenever your resistance of popular sentiment or belief about a creature or situation is vindicated.

Judge Camps

Judges are the practical decision-makers and sometimes leaders of the imbued, whether they claim those positions for themselves or rise to them by virtue of planning, analyzing and seeking answers instead of acting rashly or being paralyzed by choices. They weigh the issues at stake in any situation, whether to kill a hapless person possessed by a raging spirit or to spare a bloodsucker who had no choice in her condition. They perceive right and wrong action and measure them in monsters and other hunters, not by choice but by moral, ethical or spiritual imperative. Such are the marshals' tasks, and fulfilling them embodies the loose code of the creed.

Individual Judges approach their obligations and duties very differently, though. Some uphold their values as near-unattainable guides for behavior and thought. If a creature or person cannot achieve those ideals, they are deemed guilty and must be punished. Other lawgivers do not hold the bar quite so high. They recognize the fallibility of humans and perhaps even of the creatures of the night. The latter are clearly more malicious and abusive, but humanity is capable of its own depravity, so monsters cannot be measured too harshly or the Judge risks hypocrisy. Some arbiters are even forgiving of the sins of man and monster, believing that the two are one and the same. These Judges weigh the actions of creatures as if they're peers, not abominations. At least, "monsters" are no more so than any person can be, so all must be viewed on their own merit, not by any preconceived notions or biases. These three camps are called conservative, moderate and liberal, respectively.

Conservative

Conservative Judges take a very hard line on right and wrong, virtuous and corrupt, good and bad. There are no shades of gray between the two on any level or in any circumstance. There is only the correct course of action, which is probably defined by a very narrow set of terms such as austerity, respect, charity and goodwill. And there is the wrong choice, thought or action, which can be anything that falls short of that extreme set of ideals. The conservative may set a strict regimen for his own behavior to embody the values he upholds, making himself a living example of the rules he imposes on others. Or he might aspire to these goals in hopes of becoming a better person in contrast to the harshness of the world, or perhaps to atone for some past failing. The latter Judge makes decrees upon others in hopes of convincing them to follow his course, thus spreading the effort to become idealized people in a degenerate reality.

Whether the hard-liner approaches his role from a religious or temporal perspective depends on his background. Religion might dictate his terms of right and wrong and allow no room for dissension, perhaps not even from a follower of another faith. A strict, religiously inspired Judge might believe that sending corrupt souls to Hell is best for the world, and he might condemn a hunter of another faith who believes in redeeming such lost souls while they're still on Earth. Or the conservative might establish his guides for behavior based on offenses committed against him or those around him in life — maybe even at the imbuing. Crime, neglect, infringement or even ill intent cannot be tolerated because they caused so much harm *before*. Now the Judge has the power to do something about them.

Although they are extreme, hardcore Judges are not Avengers. The vengeful assault perceived enemies without a second thought and without remorse. Dogged Judges evaluate all subjects before enforcing any punishment, to at least allow a creature a chance — albeit a small one — for salvation. They may not relish delivering punishment, either; doing harm or destroying may simply be an unavoidable necessity.

These Judges are often set in their ways before being imbued. They may have been headstrong or opinionated. They might have gotten their way because they had power or position, as with an authoritative business leader, politician, police officer or even bully. Or a conservative arbiter might have held high standards previously in life, but never had the leverage, weight or opportunity to impose them — until now.

Favored Attributes: Like all Judges, these people rely on Perception and Intelligence to recognize and identify transgressions. They need Strength and Endurance to back up their authority.

Favored Abilities: Talents such as Expression, Intimidation, Leadership and Subterfuge are important for recognizing and contending with offenders, and for organizing other imbued according to the conservative's code. Knowledges are less important to someone who simply *knows* right from wrong.

Favored Backgrounds: Allies, Bystanders, Destiny, Grace Under Pressure (see p. 71), Influence and Steel Nerves (see p. 73) are important to Judges who have clear perceptions of the world's denizens, and a plan for how to segregate them.

Other Favored Paths: Beyond following the Judgment path, these people often turn to Vengeance and Defense edges as weapons for the cause. Innocence and Vision powers are useless when one doesn't deny or question one's course or enemies.

MODERATE

The moderate Judge upholds values or goals as ideals in life and the hunt, and he measures people and the world from this frame of reference. He might put faith in honesty, honor, duty or temperance. He recognizes, however, that those are *his* ethics. Though others should uphold them as well for the betterment of society and mankind, not everyone does or even can. It's within human capacity to lie, betray and neglect. These sins have always existed and always will. Their embodiment and proliferation by the

monsters of the world will ensure that. People therefore really aren't that different from monsters.

And yet, humanity is capable of far better. Anyone can intellectually understand that crime, abuse and sin are wrong. Avoiding them can be a simple exercise. One always has choices, whether to commit a wrong or to do what's right. Choice is what separates humans from monsters. Whereas the latter seem determined to commit evil, the former can rise above it if they decide to. After all, if monsters could do the right thing, too, why would they hide their existence, lurk at night and prey upon their potential betters? Perhaps they're simply people who have made the wrong choices too many times and now can't stop themselves.

The moderate Judge is therefore constantly faced with decisions and uncertainties. Not only must he try to do his best and follow his own morals, he must hope that others do too, and decide when they succeed or fail. Unfortunately, most people — and certainly monsters — fail. The low road is easier to take in any situation, and doing so usually leads to more paths of least resistance — and eventually to habitual depredation. If the monsters of the world didn't blaze those trails, they have certainly paved them since.

The best a moderate Judge can do is strive for the high road and lead others on the same path. Some might need a hand up along the way. Others might fall. These mediators simply shepherd other people along and watch for the wolf waiting hungrily in the shadows.

The truly difficult part is, when does a person or monster unremittingly defy the values a Judge cherishes, and when can punishment be meted out? Ethics are codes of behavior, so defying them should be obvious. Yet, forgiveness or compassion might bring a person or even a monster back onto the high road. If punishment is not delivered, however, and ideals are altered to suit an individual or situation, they aren't rules or ethics any longer. The moderate Judge therefore wrestles constantly with the definitions of right and wrong. He has personal concepts of what those are, but do his ideas apply to everyone at all times?

These Judges were often counselors, aides or parents in life *before*. They sought to help others make the right choices, but didn't decide for them; that would have defied personal choice. The imbuing makes such an outlook all the more demanding because the stakes are so much higher. Where misjudgment or bad counsel could result in a setback or downturn before, it can make the difference between a saved soul and a damned one now.

Favored Attributes: Perception and Intelligence are important, as ever, to know when a person is in danger of falling or if a creature is capable of salvation. Wits can make the difference between suspecting and knowing, however. Charisma can set someone back on the right course. Manipulation can trick her into playing her hand.

Favored Abilities: Intuition is valuable for interpreting people's and monsters' intentions, whereas Knowledges such as Academics, Politics and Law establish a record of human failings and vices, reinforcing a personal sense of what's right and wrong. Investigation helps confirm on which side of the line a subject falls.

Favored Backgrounds: Exposure, Fame and Resources are likely to reveal the best and worst of the human condition — what generosity and graciousness people are capable of, and what greed and vanity people can demonstrate. Having a Mentor often colors one's concept of the world, depending upon that person's take on things.

Other Favored Paths: After Judgment, Redemption edges are useful for evaluating the light and dark sides of an identity. Vision powers can help a moderate arbiter decide what the best course to take is, whether as a leader or presiding judge, jury and possibly executioner. Martyrdom powers hold little appeal. It makes no sense to punish oneself for another's sins.

LIBERAL

The liberal Judge literally has no preconceived notions about right or wrong, virtue or vice, human or "monster." Her world is a range of moral grays, never blacks or whites. How can there be any overriding immutable truths or wrongs when everyone's situation and needs are different? No single person can decide what's right for another without investigating that person's predicament, without walking a mile in his shoes.

The tolerant Judge seeks to weigh the best answer in each individual situation, aspiring to the greatest good at all times. She is therefore a believer in "morals" rather than "ethics" — an individual sense of what is acceptable and unacceptable versus one delivered from on high. Virtue and sin are therefore valid on a case-by-case basis only. A tyrant who commits genocide for political support or out of pure hatred is evil. A person who kills in self-defense or to stop a mass murderer from continuing his spree acts for the greater good.

The danger of this free-thinking outlook means that the liberal Judge must face the consequences of her decisions. She has no one but herself to blame when she makes an incorrect decision or choice. An apparent mass murderer might actually have condemned a group of *greater* offenders; their crimes were simply not immediately apparent. A blood drinker spared now because it strives not to kill might go on to murder savagely when its hunger overwhelms it. The open-minded Judge does her best on the mission, but bears a terrible burden when her efforts or intuition fails.

These evaluators are not inclined to become leaders of the imbued, because leading means delivering their own values or determining the perceptions of others. Liberals are more comfortable as subordinates and confidants who can offer alternative points of view and perhaps broad insights. Awareness and corroboration of a being's behavior are important to these people, but intuition is just as valuable. "Evidence" such as bloody walls with which a ghost torments homeowners doesn't make a haunting unjust if the inhabitants killed the person whose spirit haunts them.

These Judges take little to no pleasure from the hunt. Every day and night presents new choices to make and fates to decide. It would all be much easier if such a Judge could abide by a strict set of values and condemn all who fail to meet them. But liberal Judges often recognize uncertainty about their own values, and about how to decide what the ideal choice is in any situation. They just do what they can and hope for the best. When they're true to themselves, the best often results.

Although they seek to bring an unblemished eye to the hunt, liberal Judges are not Innocents. Whereas Innocents hope for the best from other people and beings, sometimes to a fault, open-minded Judges offer only so much latitude. These arbiters can quickly decide that the greater good is served when a being is simply not a part of it, whether that means a situation, a locale or this world. There are rarely second chances with these people, because condemnation by them usually means some heinous or remorseless act has already been committed. That's when the liberal can be as determined as the conservative.

Tolerant Judges were typically open to new ideas or possibilities earlier in life. They might have been teachers, scientists, optimistic youths or religious devotees. Liberal Judges can also previously have been hard-cases — people with little regard for the world or humanity in general — whose viewpoints are turned inside out when the extent of corruption is made clear. Maybe humanity has been deserving all along once compared to the depths to which it could fall.

Favored Attributes: Perception and Intelligence are important, as with the other camps. Charisma and Manipulation are also useful in helping or tricking beings into accepting or fulfilling the greater good.

Favored Abilities: Expression is ideal for persuading a creature to understand the harm of its ways, though Skills such as Drive, Survival and Stealth are effective when a thing won't see the light.

Favored Backgrounds: Allies, Arsenal and Contacts are all useful Traits when one's approach to the hunt involves a degree of trust toward potentially inhuman entities.

Other Favored Paths: After Judgment, Innocence and Defense edges are useful to gain perspective (and distance) when pursuing a creature's true identity and intentions. Visionary powers are helpful to determine these things in advance. Vengeance edges have limited application, because they allow for only one "greater good": destruction.

TRAITS

Judges approach the hunt with idealized concepts of what's right and wrong or best for the world. They hope to fulfill those values by gathering information, contemplating creatures' potential, identifying dangers and coordinating other imbued to achieve goals. All of these tasks demand certain Traits of Judges, such as Perception,

Leadership, Investigation and Intuition. Some Backgrounds are specifically suited to lawgivers to help them as frames of reference on how to carry out the hunt, however, perhaps to remind them what was important before or to hone faculties when insight is needed most. These Traits may be acquired before the imbuing and help decide that a person becomes a Judge, or they may develop in pursuit of the calling as tools to ensure that one presides fairly.

These Traits are ostensibly available to all characters but should not be taken or assigned to the detriment of a Judge's individuality in a group. The Storyteller should always decide whether other creed members may possess these qualities.

BACKGROUNDS

DATABASE

Harry simply nodded and said, "Yes Ma'am" as the crisis center's night supervisor criticized his recent job performance. Through it all, his only concern was that she might smell the stink of garbage on his clothes.

After she finished with him, Harry walked quickly to his cubicle. Fortunately, there weren't any operators working close enough to get a whiff of him. Harry settled into his chair and turned on his computer. While it came to life, he pulled the stained and crumpled phone bill from his coat pocket and smoothed it flat on his desktop.

The creature's servants were careful, Harry mused. The blood slave Leibowitz never dealt with his master in person. Under casual inspection, the man led a typical nine-to-five existence. In truth, he worked at a law office, came home at night and took instructions via cell phone from a monster. The beast never revealed itself, working its evil in almost perfect isolation.

Almost. Harry ran a grubby finger down the list of numbers on the billing statement. One number stood out in particular, showing up in more than three-quarters of the entries. Each call was made after six in the evening. Harry smiled.

Harry entered his password into the computer. The crisis center's database was updated weekly by the local phone company. If someone called in but was cut off for any reason, the operators had to be able to tell the authorities where the call had originated.

He keyed in the number from the phone bill. Two seconds later, he had a name and address.

The right information can mean the difference between life and death for a hunter. For Judges in particular, no fact is too minor when contemplating the guilt of a monster or its servants. Though many fiends have learned over time to hide their activities behind layers of deception, they are still subject to the invasive touch of the Information Age. Everyone from direct-mailing companies to government organizations maintains extensive electronic databases that track everything from financial transactions to dog-food preferences. A careful researcher with the right connections can put together a detailed profile of an individual's assets, interests and activities in a matter of hours — from the relative safety of a home computer.

This Background allows a character to access one or more commercial or civil databases. Rating determines the depth, detail and scope of the information that the character can obtain. The exact nature of the database(s) that a character can access is at the Storyteller's discretion, and must be in keeping with the character's concept. An ex-cop might still have access to the city's crime records and DMV database. A bank teller might be able to reach local, national or even international financial resources using the boss' password.

The difference between using databases and human Contacts is that a human contact can tell a hunter what a subject does, but not necessarily why. Conversely, a database profile provides clues to an individual's activities over a broad spectrum, but little in the way of specific actions. A blood slave's financial records might show that a large sum of money was deposited into his bank account recently. Then a tip from a local contact reveals that the slave has been seen in the company of a local gang member and black marketeer. The two sources of information let the hunter form a more complete picture.

- •   You have access to a local database that provides basic personal information (a city phone company that provides unlisted phone numbers and a cross-referenced list of numbers and addresses, for example).

- ••   You can enter local government databases such as city police, vehicle registration and property records.

- •••   You have connections to databases that contain sensitive personal data, such as credit histories, bank statements and social security information.

- •••• With time, you can call upon nationwide resources such as the FBI's powerful criminal database (which tracks criminal activity and known sightings of suspects), or giant databases like LEXUS-NEXUS (which can provide social security numbers, bank records, financial transactions and medical histories on a nationwide basis). Gaining results from these sources can take from four to 48 hours, at the Storyteller's discretion.

- ••••• You can enter a variety of state and federal data bases, which provide everything from ATM trans actions to sealed military records. Access to world wide law enforcement or financial databases such as INTERPOL or Lloyd's of London are possible. Results from these databases can take one to five working days, but provide a wealth of detailed information.

GRACE UNDER PRESSURE

Carla could hear Neal's breath becoming more rapid. "What are they waiting for?" he said. She could hear a hint of hysteria in his voice.

"They're psyching us out," she whispered back, taking care to breathe in through her nose, out through her mouth, and thinking, "Come on you bastards."

"Shit," Neal whimpered. "They outnumber us three to one! How many bullets do you have left? I think I'm down to nine, but I lost count."

"It doesn't matter. We've got enough, and they have to come through the door one at a time. They're as scared as we are," she said, though mentally it was "scared as you are."

"But what if…?" Neal never finished his question. The door burst open, and before it rebounded off the opposing wall, Carla put a shot in the lead attacker's eye. Neal was shrieking as the second thing came through, but Carla took that one in the throat, breathing in through her nose, out through her mouth. By the time the third was halfway over the crumpled bodies, Neal had recovered enough to open fire. He was still screaming.

Western movies make a big deal about a shooter having a quick draw. In reality, the ability to draw a weapon quickly is of little use if you can't use it steadily. Danger — especially the life-threatening kind — is intimidating. A normal human reaction to a sudden threat is inaction, psychological paralysis. If the outcome is mortally important, people tend to freeze as they try to choose the best option. Consequently, they do nothing, which is usually the *worst* option.

Some people, however, are free of this limitation. Intensely trained or indoctrinated fighters — or people who just have a lot of common sense — are better equipped than most to react to danger. They may not be physically faster than others, but sureness in their actions prevents them from working counter to their own purposes. A cop on a tough beat, a seasoned soldier or someone who has survived a civil war might develop this kind of focus.

This Background imposes a minimum on your Initiative rolls. If the number that comes up on your die (before it's added to Dexterity + Wits) *is less than or equal to* your dots in Grace Under Pressure, you can re-roll (though you do not have to). If your second roll is still less than or equal to your rating in this Background, you have to choose one of the two results.

- •   Calm. You can re-roll a 1.
- ••   Laconic. You can re-roll a 2 or less.
- •••   Tranquil. You can re-roll a 3 or less.
- ••••   Possessed of great *sang-froid*. You may choose to re-roll any Initiative result of 4 or less.
- ••••• Unshakeable equanimity. If you wish, you can attempt to better any Initiative roll of 5 or less.

SOULMATE

"So then, you're saying it's up close and personal?"

"Well, yeah. I mean, they're dug in and, you know, we can't get a clean shot at them from outside. So we're going in, but we've got a good plan…."

"Sorry. I'm out. I'd like to help, but I can't."

"Look, I know you'd rather take a long-distance approach, but this is five on two. It's practically a sure thing!"

"I have responsibilities."

"But…. I mean…."

"Look, I said no and I said I was sorry. There's not much more to say, is there?"

"This is about Gwyn, isn't it?"

"Leave her out of it."

"No, it is, isn't it? She doesn't want you doing anything 'dangerous,' right? Shit!"

"This is my decision and she—"

"Bullshit, it's your decision. That bitch has stolen your balls. That's what's making the decision!"

"Don't you fuckin' call her a bitch!"

"Or what? You gonna fight me? Huh? I thought you didn't get 'up close and personal' anymore. She too scared your pretty face is gonna get all scratched and shit?"

"Listen to me, asshole. She doesn't know. You got me? She knows nothing. I haven't told her about any of it. You know why? Remember what happened with Julie and Dennis? That thing couldn't find her, so it killed him. I'm not going to let that happen to Gwyn."

"Hell… I don't want to see anything happen to her either, but… we need you, man."

"Not like she does."

True love is hard to find — especially in the World of Darkness. But your character has found it and the thought of his beloved gives him strength to get back up when he's down and out. After all, he knows who he's fighting for.

Once per session, you can add a number of dice equal to Soulmate to one action and its accompanying roll, but only if it directly affects the well-being of your character's beloved. The benefit does not apply to all actions performed in a multiple action; just one. Nor does it apply to all rolls in an extended action; just one. The Storyteller has ultimate discretion on when this bonus is applicable, although you may certainly try to convince her that it does. The Storyteller may even allow it to apply to *all* rolls in a resisted action if the outcome of the competition is short term and still has direct bearing on your character's love.

Example: Brad has found that "special someone" in Gwyn; he has 3 Soulmate. This Background doesn't do much for him when he's on the prowl for zombies. But if Brad comes home to hear Gwyn screaming inside their burning house, his player can add three dice to one roll in a rescue attempt. It could be a Strength roll to break down a door. It could be a soak roll to resist smoke inhalation or an Athletics roll to carry Gwyn out.

There is a price to pay for love's rewards. Love makes your character vulnerable. This is true in the best of circumstances, and it's doubly true for a hunter who makes powerful and mysterious enemies. If your character's true love is threatened, he can't ignore it. He must do everything in his power to protect her. Your character spends the following days, weeks, months or even the rest of his life (Storyteller's discretion) consumed by depression and self-loathing should he ever try and fail to protect her from harm. In game terms, Willpower rating (not pool) is decreased for the duration by the amount of your character's Soulmate score, to a minimum of 1. He also loses the Soulmate bonus for that period of time. (If loved one and Willpower loss are permanent, the Storyteller *may* allow lost Background points to be re-invested elsewhere, after an extended period of mourning. **Hunter Book: Avenger**'s Berserk Background is a good choice.)

On top of all this, failure to prevent serious or mortal harm to a beloved may impose a derangement.

This occurs at the Storyteller's prerogative, assuming your character hasn't suffered enough.

- • You and your beloved have just embarked on your grand *amour*. You're still in the giddy romantic stage.
- •• You've been with your lover for up to a year, and you're starting to believe that this love is true (even though it seems too good to be true).
- ••• You and your lover are probably living together and have been for a while. Her flaws are no longer cute, but you've gained a rich appreciation of her virtues that more than offset her foibles.
- •••• You and your beloved have been together so long that you rely on each other the way you count on the sun rising. That doesn't mean you take each other for granted, any more than you take a beautiful sunrise for granted.
- ••••• Words fail.

STEEL NERVES

Many of the undead had heightened senses. Leanne wasn't one of them. Her first awareness of Henry's presence was a scent of bourbon and the feel of a pistol muzzle on the back of her neck.

"Howdy. Remember me?" His simple words were thick with loathing. "Stand up slow and we'll take this outside."

Leanne narrowed her eyes, calculating the odds that he'd be willing to shoot her in the middle of a crowded restaurant. He had bothered to drape a coat over his gun hand, but it was still an indiscreet approach by her standards. If he really didn't care about collateral damage, he'd have opened fire instead of introducing

himself. She glanced at the table next to her: Dressed-up teenagers on their way to prom? She liked her chances.

She stood, then turned to him. As she did, she lashed out — not with her body, but with her soul, harnessing the dread of her true nature into an intimidating glare that could bring strong men to their knees.

"Do you dare challenge me… mortal?"

The patrons behind him looked up and fled screaming. Henry just smirked.

"It takes more than that bullshit to scare me, bitch." He fired as she dove to the side. The shell broke two ribs but didn't slow her as her right hand hooked into a claw and slashed for the throat… of one of the teenagers. Blood spurted, diners screamed and Leanne smiled. Henry turned pale. She timed her attack to match his first surge of vomit.

"Scared now?" she whispered as her nails stabbed into his heart.

Spending Conviction to activate second sight and resilience to mental influence provides a defense against supernatural horror. But it has no effect against *mundane* horror. Many of the things hunters battle aren't monsters because they grow fur or drink blood. They're monsters because they willfully endanger the defenseless — and make good on their threats. They're monsters because they're satisfied with killing a hunter's family if they can't get at him directly. They're monsters because of the things they're *willing to do*.

Characters with this Background have a firmly established sense of self, a bulwark against experiences that would drive a "normal" person — even a "normal" hunter — over the edge. The stresses of the day-to-day hunt, such as losing a job or even a loved one, and the

terrible sights to which the imbued are exposed such as mutilated corpses, take less of a toll than they might.

There are numerous ways a person could develop this resilience: Powerful religious devotion, a psychologically healthy family history, the confidence that comes from outstanding personal achievement. Alternatively, people who've been exposed to horror or depravity repeatedly — social workers, emergency medical technicians, photojournalists documenting genocide — simply develop high thresholds for shock.

Roll your character's Steel Nerves rating, difficulty 8, when she would normally suffer a short- or long-term derangement. Your character resists the ailment completely with even a single success. Note that this Background applies to only those derangements acquired from exposure to trauma or horrible sights. It does not apply against derangements acquired through gaining Virtues rated 7 or higher. The latter dysfunctions are more a product of the Messengers' otherworldly interference with your hunter's mind and life than with any capacity he has to stare directly at a grisly scene.

The Storyteller has the option of rolling this Background on your behalf if she wants to keep story developments — and your character's possible resilience to them — mysterious.

- Gruesome horror movies don't even make you blanch.
- • You could watch autopsy films unfazed.
- • • You could eat a chili dog at a murder scene.
- • • • You could endure torture without losing your wits.
- • • • • You could cope with the death of a family member at monstrous hands, at least for the short term.

The High Cost of Commitment

Maintaining a Judge's perspective on the hunt is a delicate proposition. These imbued endure enormous stress given the responsibilities they assume. Not only must they make decisions for themselves and allied imbued — Which target do we pursue? Can we risk letting this creature go? How many defenseless people can be allowed to die before we strike? — Judges must rise above the din and remain alert to further dangers, anticipate immediate problems and gather ever more information. Being imbued is punishment enough on the fragile human mind. All these burdens only worsen the wear.

The result is typically that capable Judges emerge and prove their strength, awareness and perseverance. Meanwhile, lessers collapse under the weight of their load, whether they are killed, forced to abandon the hunt, driven mad or made obsessed with some seemingly innocuous or bizarre aspect of the mission.

These fates are as much a result of high Virtue ratings as they are of nightly rigors. Many who seek balance in Virtues beyond Zeal may fall victim to the horrors that a prolonged hunt inflicts. Imbued who focus on Zeal and their authoritative role eventually burn out or pursue abstract notions that other imbued cannot comprehend.

Spending Conviction

Judges rarely do anything without first gathering all facts they can and considering all the permutations. That means hearing a creature out before pardoning or condemning it. That means evaluating one threat to ensure that another isn't more immediate. That means focusing on perceived right and wrong to ensure that the best course is always followed.

Considering and weighing with regard to Conviction means deciding what's most important in a situation before energy is expended. For you, that means deciding whether it's more important to hold onto 10 Conviction in the face of a threat, to use those points against an enemy, or to cash them in for a new Virtue point (and possibly a new edge). If no perceptible danger looms, you may exchange your Conviction, but a Judge is always concerned that some unseen menace lurks, waiting to catch her when she's most vulnerable. Any Virtue or edge gained hopefully offsets the danger of having low Conviction after cashing in, but the Messengers and their fickle will can never be taken for granted. It's a judgment you have to make.

Virtues chosen when Conviction is cashed in are typically based on a Judge's state of mind, whether conservative, moderate or liberal. See "Other Favored Paths" under the camp definitions for Virtue and edge ideas.

Regaining Conviction

Judges' purpose and dedication are affirmed when the plans they create and the decisions they make in the hunt succeed. Coordinating other imbued to accomplish a goal or accurately anticipating and countering the dangers of a situation bolsters Judges' confidence for their calling. In contrast, making decisions that get people hurt or killed, or planning an operation that fails partially or utterly can devastate arbiters, undermining any self-assurance they may have in their role as imbued.

These highs and lows impact the game directly through Conviction points; Judge characters can gain or lose them. The Storyteller has final say about how Conviction is awarded or withdrawn, but the following instances are specific to Judges and their waxing or waning vigor. Each of these actions should confer no more than one Conviction point per game session. Indeed, one point may be all that a character gains by pulling off several of these actions in a single chapter.

• Gain a point of Conviction when a plan of action involving the supernatural — that's chosen or created solely by your character — is a resounding success.

• Gain a point of Conviction when your character gathers information on the supernatural and uses it to accomplish an intended goal, rather than to act rashly without intelligence.

• Gain a point of Conviction when your character's lofty ideals of right and wrong are affirmed, perhaps when adhered to by others with rewarding results or when dissenters suffer failure or harm.

- Gain a point of Conviction when personal choice or preference is set aside to perform an action necessary to the cause, despite distaste for the deed.

- (Optional) *Lose* a point of Conviction when a plan or course of action chosen by your character results in the harm of allies or defenseless people.

- (Optional) *Lose* a point of Conviction when your character fails to fulfill a greater good or does not adhere to his own definition of morals, ethics or "right."

- (Optional) *Lose* a point of Conviction when your character acts rashly, without intelligence, or ponders options or courses of action too long to the point of being ineffectual.

New Derangements

Like all hunters, Judges can become increasingly unstable as their devotion to the hunt takes them further and further from their former lives. Resulting ailments vary with the individual, but Judges do display certain tendencies or patterns in their dementia. Because arbiters bear such responsibility through their leadership of and decision-making for other imbued, they are sometimes overwhelmed by the ramifications of their decrees. The death of an ally or an unwitting person can torment Judges, perhaps for the remainder of their lives. Decisions to kill or spare a creature that later prove disastrous can be taken wholly to heart. The inability to make a conclusive decision or choose a specific course of action before it's too late — a monster gets away or a loved one is punished as a warning to the hunter — weighs heavily on the soul.

The results of these pressures can force a Judge to try to abandon the hunt. Whether that is possible when monstrous visions persist and the Messengers continue to harass the mediator depends on how thoroughly she shuts herself out. Suicide attempts are perhaps highest among Judges of all the imbued, given the grief and guilt they carry. Another response is to deny any sense of responsibility by throwing oneself into the "work." Judges who do so tend to become obsessed with one aspect of the hunt, whether it be dealing with a specific kind of creature, upholding a specific value such as honesty to the exclusion of all else, or perhaps even stalking those hunters whom a Judge feels are traitors to the cause. This determined focus is a distraction in which the lawgiver may hide from the events of her past.

Of course, these ailments may develop due to any 7 or higher Virtue rating, as a Judge loses more and more of her previous identity and increasingly lives for the hunt. They also arise from personal tragedies, horrific sights and excruciating pain suffered along the way. The Storyteller decides when your character endures a hardship so extreme that her psyche is damaged.

Treatment for derangements, whether Virtue- or trauma-induced, might be possible. For Judges, it typically means coming to terms with guilt and responsibility. It might mean earning forgiveness from the families of fallen allies or accomplishing some astounding greater good that tempers previous failures just a little. That, and lots of Willpower could be spent over the course of the chronicle to actively overcome madness. There are no hard-and-fast rules for alleviating derangements. Only roleplaying, character development and Storyteller discretion can tell — and high-Virtue-induced derangements might not be curable at all.

Denial

Hunters cannot guess at how long monsters have walked the Earth. The creatures' hidden existence suggests that they have not only existed but reigned for ages, as one might conclude from normal humans' ongoing ignorance. For some hunters, the sheer stress of being aware creates mental blocks or subconsciously skews perceptions. The result can be a refusal to accept some individuals as monsters at all. Perhaps a bloodsucker drained a child in a Judge's presence, and afterward she can accept only the idea that the child and a man were "playing." Encountering that vampire later threatens to remind the hunter of the sight and the pain it spurs. Perhaps a Judge refuses to believe that any creature is more dangerous than a shapechanger — a monster hiding in human form — and dedicates himself to dealing with those beings alone, regardless of what danger other creatures might demonstrably pose. Or a Judge could refuse to acknowledge the death of an ally in a mission orchestrated by the Judge. To his mind, the hunter still lives and perhaps continues to work at his side; maybe a living ally "becomes" that fallen comrade to the leader's mind.

If confronted by indisputable evidence of reality — say that same vampire kills another person before the denying Judge's eyes — a Willpower roll, difficulty 8, may be made to accept the truth for the remainder of the scene. In the above case, your character forces himself to recognize the demon in the person and is able to deal with the vampire for a short time. Sufficient reality-affirming situations may finally make a hunter comprehend the truth, or at least allow you to spend Willpower points at will for your character to comprehend fully for a scene.

If a hunter denies the existence of an individual creature, she might not even perceive the being as wrong with second sight or a perception edge such as Discern. She is immune to mental, emotional and bodily influence by the creature, however, as if Conviction had been activated, even if none is spent in a scene. This "free" protection does not apply in any scene in which the hunter comes out of denial temporarily.

Indecision

Perhaps your character made a decision that got one or more allies killed, or that resulted in the death of someone he was trying to save. Plagued by memories of bad choices, your character can be paralyzed when it comes to making snap decisions. Unfortunately, the immediate choices that hunters must make often involve life and death.

The Storyteller decides when your character might waver when confronted with an important decision that must be made instantly. The circumstances should be reminiscent of past traumatic events. Perhaps a current participant appears similar to a person harmed in a previous judgment call. Maybe the gruesome displays of a ghost cause flashbacks to a similar experience in which your character killed a hapless possession victim. Or chasing a creature through crowded city streets might remind your character of the terrifying shock of his imbuing on a busy subway platform.

Regardless of the circumstances, the Storyteller makes a Willpower roll, difficulty 8, on your behalf. If the roll fails, you do not roll a die for Initiative, but simply total Initiative rating (Dexterity + Wits) to determine the order in which your character acts in each turn for the remainder of the scene. Furthermore, your character cannot advise other characters how to act. Nor can he coordinate their activities. He is wracked by conflicting ideas of how to respond to the situation and memories of how previous decisions failed.

It's possible to spend a Willpower point to forcibly snap out of indecision for the remainder of a scene. Another person confronting your character to "do something" might also allow you the opportunity to spend Willpower.

This ailment does not deter your character from forming *advance* plans for dealing with creatures or situations. He may not be able to follow through with those plans, however, if his past returns to haunt him during the fast-paced course of events. Nor does this derangement preclude your character from making casual decisions such as buying a gift for his sister, or even when to make a sharp turn while driving (unless some past tragedy involved a car accident…).

Some Judges' bouts of indecision can be so crippling to their faith in their own abilities that they lose Conviction points after episodes, and they may even try to avoid hunting altogether.

EDGES

One of the reasons that hunters' creeds are so vague is that the imbued seem to possess myriad edges. Not only do hunters with different outlooks on the hunt have some similar capabilities but some imbued with similar philosophies have wildly different powers.

The problem is compounded by variations on edges that like-minded hunters seem to share. A Judge in Mexico or even in an inner city may develop Vigilance instead of Discern, because her immediate survival requires constant alertness instead of deep perception. Since hunters can't always tell when edges are similar or different, they may assume that fellow specialists actually belong to different creeds — if an imbued even senses a connection between mentality and edges.

The following edges are suited to Judges and their purpose in the hunt, but are not exclusive to those imbued. Members of other creeds may learn about these capabilities as word of them spreads and as Judges pursue their roles as information gatherers and disseminators, and as leaders.

• VIGILANCE

The clearest eye is still blind when shut. Some hunters in areas of particularly extreme monster infestation develop the ability to subsist on increasingly less sleep in order to confront the supernatural. Reduced rest periods also diminish the threat posed to imbued minds during sleep, when Conviction's defenses might not be available.

These hunters still need some rest, and they drop into virtually catatonic states when they do sleep. Applying this capability takes its toll, though, as the hunter becomes more disoriented and less purposeful over time.

System: The more Zeal a judge has, the less sleep with which she can get by, as follows:

Zeal	Sleep Needed per 24 Hours of Activity
1-2	6 Hours
3-4	5 Hours
5-6	4 Hours
7	3 Hours
8	2 Hours
9	1 Hour
10	Minutes or perhaps none

A character can be roused prematurely from such concentrated rest by anything that would wake a normal person — a loud noise, shaking or perhaps even an intuitive sense that the supernatural threatens (see Reacting with Conviction, **Hunter,** p. 133). A character thus roused is slightly disoriented; all nonreflexive actions performed thereafter are at +1 difficulty until the minimum amount of sleep needed is achieved.

After each 24-hour period that this edge is used, your character loses one point from his Willpower pool. All Willpower lost this way is regained after a normal full night's sleep (at least as normal as a night can be for the tormented imbued).

Furthermore, any time you fail a roll to react instinctively to activate Conviction when its defenses are otherwise down, you get to re-roll the attempt (or the Storyteller may re-roll any failure for your character). This edge simply makes your hunter more alert to the subtle signs or warnings of supernatural presence or manipulation than other imbued are. This intuitive capacity to sense danger applies whenever your character does not have Conviction active, even when sleeping after an extended period of activity, also made possible by this same edge.

This power can be used only by the possessing hunter — it can't be "shared" to keep other imbued up or alert. Your character cannot have this edge and the Insomnia derangement (described in **Hunter Book: Redeemer**). If both of the conflicting Traits develop during play, one of them overrides the other (the Storyteller decides which and for how long). Furthermore, this edge cannot be combined with the Endurance Trait from **Hunter Book: Defender**.

With this power, Conviction can be *risked* on rolls to react to supernatural danger when defenses are otherwise down. Conviction can't be risked where staying awake is concerned.

● ● ANATHEMA

Anyone who observes the unnatural for long perceives that many have… appetites. Vampires feast on blood, often returning to the same victims time and again. Ghosts seem to draw energy from familiar places and emotional people, as do some beings that are less easily identified.

Anathema allows a Judge to decree one individual (herself included) or place as distasteful, painful or simply abhorrent when it comes to feeding. The imbued must trace hunter code's Judgment symbol upon the person or area. This marking need not be done visibly, as with ink or spray paint — drawing it invisibly with a finger suffices if (and only if) physical contact is made.

Humans who see a *visible* sign do not comprehend its significance. Hunters who see such a symbol can intuitively recognize it as drawn by a Judge or another hunter who understands such people and their calling. Other imbued see nothing if the symbol is only traced with a finger, not made legibly. Some beings with supernatural perceptions may perceive an "invisible" symbol as a vague, blurry outline or as a disconnected presence, though they probably don't know what to make of it. Most creatures notice nothing until they actually try to feed and discover that the effort is nauseating.

System: This edge is a subtler version of the more overt level-three power Balance. Anathema is person- or place-specific, whereas Balance allows a Judge to confront a predator directly. Because the Judgment emblem is involved, and hunters of other creeds do not usually sense identity with that symbol, arbiters are usually the only ones to use this power. They don't have to be, though, if another hunter has taken pains to study the collective Word.

Your character must spend a turn drawing the symbol to make someone or someplace resistant to monsters' feeding. Roll Strength + Zeal, difficulty 6. Each success imposes a level of bashing damage on a creature the moment it seeks to feed or take energy from the designated person or place thereafter. This damage can be soaked by most creatures, and may not prevent them from feeding altogether. It does, however, make the experience extremely gut-wrenching and therefore repellent. A victim can still be drained of blood and killed in the case of a vampire, or emotionally assailed in the case of a spirit. The attacker simply suffers from the effort — little solace to a victim who doesn't understand the part she plays in an invisible war.

The ban lasts one day per point of Zeal (or until your character decides to withdraw it). It even persists if the invoking hunter is Incapacitated later. A hunter can protect a number of people or places equal to her Zeal rating, simultaneously, and does not have to be in proximity to any of them. Repeated application of this power to the same subject does not have cumulative effect.

If an area is made "punishing," any creature that restores its energy reserves in that vicinity must endure pain (as bashing damage). The size of the area depends on Zeal rating.

Zeal	Area
1-2	One average-sized room in a house
3-4	Three average-sized rooms in a house
5-6	An entire two-story house
7	All of a large mansion or four floors of an office building
8	An acre of land or eight floors of an office building
9	An entire office building
10	A square mile of space

This power does not preclude a monster from using its Willpower (see **Hunter**, Chapter 9) or other energy source to perform supernatural feats. The edge also has no effect on other hunters and their acquisition of more Conviction or Virtues.

Anathema cannot be applied to supernatural beings as protection against being the prey of yet other creatures, either individually or when a victimized creature stands in an otherwise quarantined region.

●●● VOW

Sometimes a creature cannot be defeated. Sometimes a creature does not seem to warrant destruction. Sometimes a Judge feels obligated to offer the benefit of the doubt. These are gray zones in a war that many see as stark black and white. In such uncertain situations, it's a tremendous relief to be able to forge pacts with the supernatural, agreements that are bound by something more than blind faith and a handshake. This edge gives a Judge the ability to come to such terms with the other side.

Your character and a creature verbally negotiate an agreement in which the being promises to eschew a particular activity. ("I'll leave town and never return." "I'll never attack a human being again." "I'll never again enter a sanctified building.") That means the subject must be somewhat intelligent and capable of rational thought, at least at the time.

Your character traces the Judgment symbol upon the creature, perhaps visibly with paint or invisibly with a finger, and the pact is sealed. If the creature breaks its promise, the sign bursts into flame. Removing a painted or even tattooed sign does not invalidate the contract. As with Anathema, an invisible symbol is not preternaturally visible to humans or hunters. Creatures with paranormal perceptions may perceive it in a vague fashion, even if they don't know what it means.

Vow can only punish a particular, designated action. It can't compel a creature to actively perform an action, such as destroy itself or attack its supernatural master, even if the creature would agree to those terms. It can only proscribe a type of action and make it punishable, and only if the creature wittingly agrees beforehand. Of course, some Judges aren't above applying a great deal of coercion to elicit a vow. After all, "Swear and let me trace this thing on your head" sounds a lot more palatable if the alternative is, "Get soaked in gas and set on fire."

System: Once your character has reached an agreement with a creature, he must draw or trace the Judgment symbol somewhere on its body. Spend one point of Conviction at that time. If the creature ever violates the trust, your character knows it instantly no matter the distance between the parties. The seal bursts into flame. When that happens, roll Charisma + Zeal. (Yes, this means that the contract of a moderately experienced Judge becomes stronger as her Virtue rises.) The difficulty is the target's Stamina +3. For each success achieved, the seal inflicts a level of lethal damage, which may be soaked if the being is capable of resisting flames.

Each contract applies for one month per point of Zeal at the time of establishment. Your character may enact as many bonds at one time as she has points in Zeal, although each creature can be subject to only one at a time. If a Judge makes multiple vows, she knows immediately which creature betrays her trust when it happens (and you can choose to risk Conviction on your Charisma + Zeal roll, as you see fit). Vows can be revoked by your character after they're made, but the subject does not know that he is no longer accountable unless he performs the proscribed action and no punishment is delivered.

Vow can apply to disembodied spirits as well, as long as your character can touch the space occupied by the entity and some form of intelligible communication is possible between participants.

Vow cannot be applied to a group of creatures at the same time; they must be contracted individually. This edge has no effect on other hunters.

● ● ● ● CONFESSION

At this high level of power, a Judge's abilities come full circle. Just as Discern allows your character to gain information about physical features from a distance, Confession imparts information from a monster's very mind. By touching a creature and asking a question, your Judge senses the being's emotional and intellectual responses and may intuit the true answer. The Judge speaks the honest answer aloud, regardless of what lie the subject might give or even if the subject remains silent.

The few extremist Judges who claim to possess this power describe a temporary bond formed with the mind of a subject. The experience can be extremely discomforting with a warped or twisted individual, and some Judges fear revealing something of their own identities and thoughts in the process.

System: Your character must touch the subject and ask a single question in a language that the creature understands. Spend one Conviction and roll Manipulation + Zeal. The difficulty is the subject's Willpower. If the creature has a 9 Willpower or higher, the difficulty is 9.

If the roll is successful, your character speaks *one sentence* of the "true" answer aloud. Note that this isn't necessarily the absolute truth (if there is such a thing). It's only the truth *as the subject understands it*. For example, if a Judge questions someone who has been duped into believing that vampires are evil space aliens, that's the answer the Judge shakes loose. If an answer can't be contained within one sentence alone, then the Judge is at a loss for whatever other information might be available. Confession can be used on a single subject only once per scene, whether successfully or not.

A failed roll results in a garbled, confusing montage of surface thoughts and free associations. A botch means the subject can feed your character false information; it still comes out of your character's mouth. The Storyteller may therefore insist on making Confession rolls on your behalf. The Storyteller also has the prerogative to rule that a truly old or powerful creature's thoughts cannot be penetrated by any hunter, regardless of what level edge the imbued possesses.

This edge *can* be used on regular people and other hunters. The social implications of using it on other chosen can be… inflammatory. It also works on disembodied spirits as long as the space they occupy can be contacted and they can hear the question. The Judge utters the response, even if the ghost is incapable of speaking in the physical world.

● ● ● ● ● IMPRISON

This edge is best understood as an advanced version of Burden. A Judge can freeze an unnatural being in place, not for minutes but for hours. While it's possible that the efforts of another might budge a monster thus bound, the creature itself cannot normally depart under its own power.

System: Your character must fix a creature with his gaze in one turn's action. Spend two Conviction points and roll Stamina + Zeal. The difficulty is the creature's Stamina +3. The creature is trapped in place for one hour per each success achieved, even if your character becomes Incapacitated thereafter. Your character no longer need keep his eyes on the target once it is bound.

A Judge who has imprisoned a creature may choose to release it prematurely and must be able to see the being to do so (this edge is effective for convincing creatures to agree to a vow…). If a creature is attacked or endangered while affixed, a Willpower roll, difficulty 8, may be made for it to escape. The creature's successes must exceed those achieved in your original Stamina + Zeal roll. The same requirements must be fulfilled to escape Imprison by use of a power of unnatural movement — amazing speed, teleportation — in a roll of Stamina + the relevant Trait, difficulty 8.

This power cannot be used on regular people or other hunters.

SURVEILLANCE TECHNOLOGY

Rick and Alicia had been tailing the thing for days. They knew it wasn't human — despite its expensive suit — but had no idea what to call it. Afraid that they might lose it, Rick dared to get close enough to sit at a table next to it in a restaurant. After his short meal, he apologized for picking up the thing's coat by "accident." He wasn't sorry for slipping a locator in the pocket. That website he got it from had more for sale, anyway.

Three days later, he and Alicia were guests in a cheap hotel three blocks from the thing's expensive ad agency headquarters. They had a laser microphone set up in their room, and Rick had climbed the fire escapes of two buildings across the street from the firm to plant wireless video cameras. Now all they had to do was sit back, watch and listen.

Untrained with all this technology, Alicia still wasn't sure how everything was supposed to happen. "You spent $5,000 on this stuff. What exactly are we supposed to learn again?"

"I told you not to worry," Rick said. "I got the credit card off a dead rot — it wasn't my money. If all goes well, this guy should play his hand at some point and tell us what we're up against."

"All I see are people going back and forth. They don't even seem weird, at least not that I can see on this screen."

"Hold it," Rick said, raising one hand. "I can hear him talking."

"…running at optimal speed. We're on schedule, except for that little problem we discovered Friday. I believe agents are in place to deal with it now."

There was a polite knock at the hotel-room door….

Judges need information before they can identify monsters and devise effective strategies against them. Listening in on creatures and watching them from discreet distances are wonderful ways of gathering intelligence. They're also mundane means of conducting the hunt that arbiters can understand and trust from their previous lives. The bizarre capabilities bestowed by the Messengers may help lawgivers when help is needed most, but there's something reassuring about using good old human ingenuity and know-how against ghosts and nightcrawlers. The following section details systems for using information-gathering technology on the hunt, and it explains how to get and use such devices.

Mental Feats

• **Surveillance [Perception + Alertness/Technology or Dexterity + Stealth]:** There are two primary methods of performing covert surveillance. Your character uses either his own eyes and ears or some form of surveillance technology such as a shotgun microphone, hidden camera or bug.

Unassisted Observation: Secretly observing or listening to someone directly — without any technological tools — requires a Perception + Alertness roll. The difficulty and number of successes required depend on how far away the target is and what sort of information your character seeks. Reading a newspaper headline across a room or listening in on a moderate-volume conversation might be difficulty 5. Overhearing a whispered conversation at the next table or noticing the details of a badge someone flashes could be difficulty 9. The number of successes achieved determines how much information your character receives. One success offers vague details — a police officer's badge. Three successes typically provide all the information your character hopes for under the circumstances — the badge number. More than three successes reveal information that your character might be interested in, but which he wasn't necessarily looking for — the badge number and a birthmark on the bearer's hand.

Electronic Surveillance: Using shotgun microphones or similar surveillance devices is handled in a manner similar to unassisted observation. Roll Perception + Technology. Increasing successes do not necessarily provide further information; a single success can offer all the details your character hopes for, because the tools he uses provide comprehensive information. The difficulty of the roll is determined by the particulars of the situation. Using a shotgun microphone to eavesdrop on an unobstructed conversation in a nearby parking lot might be difficulty 5. Using a laser microphone to listen to a conversation nine blocks away by bouncing the laser off a parked car could be difficulty 8 or 9. The capabilities of the device used (see below) also influence the difficulty of such efforts.

Audio and Video Bugs: Planting a bug on a subject allows your character to track its location and listen in on all sounds made near it. Planting a bug requires doing so undetected, though, and your character doesn't want his device to be discovered later. Hiding a bug in a discreet location means rolling Dexterity + Stealth in a resisted action against the target's Perception + Alertness. Your difficulty depends on your character's ingenuity and the complexity of his effort. Walking up and patting a target's back could be difficulty 5. Slipping it into a pocket might be 7. Applying adhesive to a bug and placing it where the target might step could be difficulty 8 or 9. The difficulty for a target distracted by loud noises or bustling events might be 9. A subject performing casual activities such as eating dinner is at difficulty 7. A wary target rolls against difficulty 5 or less. Getting more successes allows your character to place a bug without being noticed. Failure alerts the target that your character is up to something untoward. A botch on your part lets the target see the bug itself.

For each success that you achieve beyond your opponent's, the difficulties of any subsequent Perception + Alertness rolls to notice the bug increase by one. Thus, the more successes you achieve in plating a device, the more discreetly it's hidden (in regard to accidental or even intended discovery). All commercially available bugs can be found readily with an electronic bug detector, however; such detection devices succeed automatically.

Planting bugs in a fixed location is handled in a somewhat similar fashion. Make a Wits + Technology roll as your character places the bug to determine how effectively he does so. Planting a bug in a large convention hall such that it will pick up the informative conversations of wandering people is difficulty 9. If the room is small or your character knows where a subject will be located, the difficulty is only 4 or 5. Failure on this planting roll indicates that the bug is unable to pick up any useful information. The Storyteller might make the roll on your behalf so that you don't know that the effort will fail in advance.

Establishing wireless video cameras in useful locales also involves the Wits + Technology roll. Because video cameras are bulkier than bugs and have limited fields of view, the difficulties of these rolls are increased by one. A separate Perception + Security roll is also needed to hide a camera effectively. The difficulty of this roll is 6 in most cases.

Once a bug or camera is in place, listening or watching involves no rolls. Using a bug to monitor the location of a mobile target requires an Intelligence + Technology roll, difficulty 5. One success indicates the subject's approximate location. Additional successes provide more specific detail.

Types of Devices

Directional Microphones: Directional microphones come in several varieties. Each of them allows the user to listen in on anything the device is pointed at. The simplest and cheapest are shotgun microphones. These devices are baton-like objects between six and 12 inches long, and an inch or so in diameter. They are lightweight, usually cost less than $100, and can be used to eavesdrop on a normal conversation at a range of 100 to 150 feet. They can be handheld or incorporated into the

sleeve of a coat or other discreet location. They cannot be used to hear through walls or at longer ranges.

Laser microphones bounce invisible light beams off any hard, reflective surface near a target. Sounds made nearby are detectable through the vibrations they create in the surface. These vibrations modulate the laser beam and are reconverted into sound after the beam has been reflected back to the user. Mirrors, windows or even shiny paint can be used as reflective surfaces. Laser microphones typically have a range of up to a mile. They can even be used to eavesdrop on conversations inside closed rooms by bouncing the laser off the room's window or a mirror within.

Laser mikes are highly accurate devices. The difficulty of using one is reduced by one. The devices usually weigh at least 10 pounds and cost a minimum of $1,500. They must also be placed on a stable surface such as a camera tripod; they can't be handheld or used from a moving vehicle.

Video Cameras: Wireless video cameras are available from any company that sells surveillance technologies, usually online. Some of these devices are no larger than a matchbook and can be bought already built into baseball caps, pagers, clocks, neckties or even eyeglasses. Other cameras are designed to be mounted on walls, with built-in lenses that allow them to "see" clearly through tiny pin holes. With broadcast ranges from 500 to 1,000 feet, hunters can hide a camera in a house and observe the goings-on from a van parked several doors away. Alternatively, one hunter wearing

a camera can be monitored by a backup team. A single wireless camera usually costs between $1,500 and $2,500.

Video cameras that connect via cables to televisions or VCRs are much less expensive and much easier to find than the wireless variety. These cameras can also be as small as a matchbook, but rely on long obvious wires that connect to TVs or VCRs. Although such cameras are rarely useful for mobile surveillance or spying on secret meetings, they can be extremely useful if mounted in and around a hunter's home. Some of these cameras use infrared light, so they can even produce useful images in nearly complete darkness. A hunter with several infrared cameras mounted around her home can turn on her TV and quickly determine whether a noise in the middle of the night is a rot entering through the kitchen window or merely her cat chasing a moth. Wired video cameras normally cost between $100 and $200.

Bugs: Wireless microphones and location devices are available from some security companies. Bugs are rarely larger than a shirt button, and the most expensive can be even smaller. Their sensitive microphones can pick up soft conversations at up to 30 feet, and their signals can be received a half-mile away. The tiny batteries in a bug typically run for one to two days. Bugs usually cost several hundred dollars each. Most allow the user to eavesdrop on a subject and track her location. The cheapest, smallest bugs track only a target's movements. Unfortunately, because bugs transmit continuously, they can be detected easily by handheld detectors. Fortunately, only spies and the paranoid typically have such locators. Bug detectors are usually about the size of a hardback novel and cost several hundred dollars. Although such devices can detect all commercially available bugs, there are no guarantees that they can detect the more advanced bugs used by the FBI or other agencies with technologies not yet available in the consumer market.

Telephone Bugs: Tiny transmitters exist that can be placed inside a phone so that everything said on that line is relayed to the eavesdropper's phone. Alternatively, you can purchase a device that can call up a phone and keep the line open when the other end is hung up. This same device employs a powerful amplifier that allows you to hear anything said within 30 feet of the monitored phone. You can even purchase a device that can access any answering machine that can be contacted remotely. You can then play all messages, change the times and dates listed, and even partially erase messages.

Telephone bugs of all types are relatively inexpensive; most cost less than $100.

Voice-stress Analyzers: These advanced devices are effectively lie detectors that measure variations in a subject's voice to determine whether he's lying. Like all forms of lie detectors, they're imperfect. Most voice-stress analyzers are the size of a small phone book and have directional microphones that can analyze the speech of any single target within 10 feet. If desired, you can even use a wireless microphone to relay signals to an analyzer located up to half a mile away. Voice-stress analyzers require no skill to use. Anyone with 1 Technology or more can operate one.

When your character uses one of these machines, the Storyteller rolls two dice, difficulty 6. Two failures mean the device registers no change, even if the subject is lying. One success means the device registers some unusual stress. Subjects exhibiting these signs are usually lying or quite upset. Two successes mean the subject is almost certainly lying.

An analyzer is designed to work only on living people. Difficulty increases by one when used on a walking corpse or otherwise dead person, and when used on a creature between human and animal shapes. Further, who can say whether a possession victim tells the truth when its possessing spirit lies....

Acquiring Surveillance Devices

Any of the surveillance devices detailed here can be purchased in the United States. Most large U.S. cities have several stores that sell such tools; a few such shops can even be found in shopping malls. Alternatively, these devices can be found on the Internet through a wide variety of companies, after a few hours' searching.

Most people are completely unaware that technologies of this sort can be purchased openly, however. Although it is perfectly possible to walk into a store and buy a tiny, wireless video camera built into a pair of sunglasses, most people assume that such devices are Hollywood fantasies or are available only to professional spies. As regular people themselves, hunters think no differently.

The two most serious limits to obtaining such devices are whether your character has heard of them and whether your character knows where to find them. In large cities such as New York, Chicago or Los Angeles, characters could easily run across stores with names like "Spy Supplies" while visiting a mall. Hunters living elsewhere aren't likely to look for or find these tools at the S-mart, no matter how smart it is to shop there.

As a rule of thumb, only characters with 3 or more Security or Technology know the full capabilities and availability of surveillance devices. More specifically, survivalists and weapons fetishists may know a great deal about surveillance devices. Someone with 2 Arsenal or greater could know of these tools and possibly have one or two that cost $100 or less. Characters with 4 Arsenal or greater might have a half-dozen cameras, bugs and similar devices, regardless of price.

For everyone else, finding out about these devices and actually obtaining them is a complex process. Looking under "Security" in the Yellow Pages locates local companies that sell such devices. In most small towns and cities, shotgun microphones, fancy burglar alarms and telephone bugs are likely to be the most that's available. Even employees of such stores are likely to be unaware that more exotic items are available for special order.

If your character decides to look for surveillance gadgets on the Internet, roll Intelligence + Research, difficulty 7. Three or more successes on a Research roll locate the sites of companies that sell any of the tools listed above, for the right price. As a more unusual option, the Storyteller could turn on a computer and have the player perform the actual search using keywords that the character is likely to think of, such as "spycameras" or "bugs."

Failing all else, shotgun microphones, simple telephone bugs, bug detectors and even matchbook-sized wired video cameras can be found in many novelty catalogs, right next to whoopee cushions and cheesy T-shirts. Anyone who buys surveillance devices from novelty catalogs has almost certainly never heard of any of the more sophisticated devices available.

Of course, this discussion applies primarily to the United States. Although gadgets are also available in Canada and Western Europe, they tend to be more difficult to locate. Also, many other countries restrict civilian possession of surveillance devices. Actually using some devices to spy on people is a crime in the United States. If a monster finds your character's camera in its lair, it doesn't need to kill you. It can have you sent to jail, instead.

Most companies also record the serial numbers of the devices they sell. If your character buys one on his credit card and the tool turns up at a crime scene, his name comes up. Careful hunters pay cash and have devices shipped to post-office boxes rented under assumed names.

Note that the items listed here are far from state of the art for such technologies. Various intelligence agencies and federal law-enforcement organizations are known to have devices that are smaller and more sensitive, with considerably longer ranges. Acquiring these devices from such agencies is far from easy. Characters who wish to obtain high-quality government surveillance machines (or who live in nations where all such devices are illegal) must have at least 3 Resources and either 3 Streetwise or 3 Contacts.

As with everything in your game, the Storyteller decides whether your character knows about, can get access to, has the funds for and/or knows how to operate surveillance technologies. Remember that **Hunter** is about the regular people of the world, the folks who shop at department stores and who tend to think "power drill" or "circular saw" when thinking "technology." If your character wouldn't even think about or look for listening devices or secret cameras, don't try to get them.

The Verdict

Many Judges are driven by the need to analyze the various monsters they encounter. Virtually all feel a responsibility to measure creatures' virtues and vices, weigh their crimes and decide their fate. Yet many Judges' plans and efforts are undermined by their very human nature and mortality; there's only so much that a single person, even a hunter, can accomplish against the monstrous forces of the supernatural. Sentencing a creature to death is fine in theory but could be impossible in practice. And if a creature has been deemed worthy of survival or condemned to destruction, only a Judge's closest allies are aware of these rulings. Other hunters who unknowingly encounter a raging devil or gentle giant have no idea that another imbued has already passed sentence on the being, and that it should be killed on sight or spared altogether.

At least, that lack of communication has persisted until now. A handful of arbiters, truly frustrated by their efforts to share such verdicts on creatures, have discovered a means to proclaim their decrees. Amazingly, these efforts seem to be bolstered by forces beyond even their own investment—as the Messengers appear to lend authority to lawgivers' sentences.

A notary public was the first Judge known to have declared her verdict over a creature for all imbued to know. Infuriated by a condescending creature that resisted her allies' attacks, she lashed out furiously and foolishly with the only weapon that came to hand at her work place: her notary seal, the indicator of her public standing that she used every day and that formed part of her identity. The brash creature permitted her to live, with no idea that it had in fact been marked as a butcher that must be destroyed. When the thing arrived at its next killing ground, potent and organized imbued detected it almost immediately and intuitively sensed its crimes, though they were unsure how or why. They simply understood that the thing had committed terrible crimes and could not be permitted to exist. With so much *unknown* on the hunt, it was a relief for these chosen to simply *know* about this being. They responded without hesitation and put the creature down, once and for all.

Thus, a Judge truly convinced of a creature's evil or worth can somehow mark the entity for other imbued to instinctively recognize as acquitted or condemned. The means of labeling differs with each imbued, but all involve

some kind of mundane sign or symbol that represents the Judge's identity, role or purpose in life or on the hunt. Touching a creature with that item essentially brands it, making its relative worthiness apparent to all imbued.

Only Judges can pass these enduring sentences. Other hunters can possess edges in the Judgment path, but they cannot understand or perform this unique practice.

METHOD

As far as anyone can tell, the capacity to mark creatures cannot be taught or passed on. Stories of the phenomenon have been shared since that first arbiter accomplished such an unprecedented feat, but the ability to do likewise has never been successfully learned. Apparently, it arises from desperation to communicate verdicts and to ensure that justice is served, no matter by whom. Judges therefore develop the technique individually after much concentration on how to convey their decrees in a lasting way.

The process involves identifying, choosing or fashioning an item that bears some sign or symbol unique the Judge's identity. It could be his monogram on a ring, his badge number on his police identification, a family motto on an heirloom or a meaningful coat of arms on a crest. The item may have existed for years and is now taken up as a tool, it could be a modified object such as a wedding band now inscribed with a marital vow, or the item could be newly created such as the last, liberating alimony check a Judge ever had to sign. The only stipulation seems to be that the item can be held entirely in one hand. Apparently, hunter code's Judgment symbol carved into an object is not enough to empower the item, perhaps because that symbol is not unique to a single person.

Once a personally important or valuable object is identified, it becomes a tool in the hunt because it seems to bear the authority of the Judge's name, identity and beliefs. It virtually becomes his "seal of approval"—or disapproval, as the case may be. Brought into contact with a supernatural being, the item brands the subject with a declaration appropriate to the Judge's perception of the creature. No hunter code or legible mark is actually made, but any other imbued who looks upon the monster gets an intuitive sense about the entity, be it that the monster "deserves punishment" or "deserves mercy."

Such labeling doesn't occur casually. The Judge must be utterly convinced of the subject's corruption or worth and be ready to harm/destroy or spare/liberate it himself given the opportunity. The arbiter must therefore have had opportunity to experience the creature's nature and get a genuine sense of its identity; casual contact is not sufficient for a lawgiver to pass judgment and mark it for all hunters to see. A Judge can innately sense when his decree has been successfully established. Attempts to impose a sentence that isn't heartfelt by an arbiter — if another hunter asks him to impose a brand and the judge has no personal experience with the creature in question, for example — do not take at all. Nothing happens in these cases.

Of course, Judges can still make errors in their assessments of monsters. A mediator might decide a being is deserving and mark it as such to spare it from other hunters' attacks. That doesn't mean the creature couldn't actually be malicious in the extreme outside the Judge's presence. Likewise, a rampaging monster might actually be a redemptive force, but has lost its senses due to matters beyond its control. A Judge who brands it evil doesn't have all the information. Only a rash or foolish justice places his sign prematurely or without investigating extensively, and thus might not be worthy of his creed.

A Judge's mark is a warning or alert to other hunters but is not law. There is no way for a Judge to ensure that his decree is honored by other imbued. A vengeful hunter who encounters a zombie with a strange "aura of worthiness" might ignore his instincts; the warrior could attack and destroy the being if he wished. Likewise, a forgiving chosen could ignore the intuitive warnings he senses from a "lost soul." Other hunters' responses to Judges' marks are left to their own discretion. There is no question about the origins of a creature's mark, though; another hunter automatically senses that an authority among his kind has had contact with this being and labeled it for all imbued to recognize. Flashbacks to sensations experienced at the imbuing can also suggest Messenger involvement in the decree.

SYSTEM

Passing sentence on creatures is only one aspect of being a Judge, and only one aspect of choosing a tool with which to communicate verdicts to other hunters. The need to share information about monsters' value or danger requires some capacity to comprehend a bigger picture of the hunt — that condemning or sparing isolated beings isn't enough to start a movement or to aid the cause as a whole. Judges' efforts need to have a more sweeping effect if they're to make substantial gains against the supernatural. In order to recognize these needs, your character requires at least 3 Zeal, 1 Mercy and 1 Vision. Once these Virtue scores are achieved, your Judge understands that he must go to lengths to unite and inform hunters, to serve justice widely and to create a tool that represents his accumulated wisdom.

No particular Crafts score is required to alter or fashion an item to be your character's sign or marker. The symbol need not even be attractive or clearly legible to work. It's who and what the item represents that's important.

Choosing or creating a marker takes some time and effort, usually a matter of days or weeks, depending on how often and for how long your character works on it. At any time of your choosing, remove a number of Conviction points from your character's current pool. Record that number in the margin of your character sheet, or the Storyteller can record it for you. Each point set aside represents about one hour's creation or search time. So, if you set aside eight points over the course of three weeks of game time, your character dedicates eight hours to his project in that period.

Ten Conviction must be invested into a completed marker. The sooner the item is finished the more quickly your character can communicate his evaluations of creatures and perhaps save (or spare) deserving souls. His Conviction pool could be drained, though, leaving him vulnerable or a liability to allies. The longer it takes to create a tool, the longer creatures go unannounced and the longer they might threaten unwary hunters' lives — or run the risk of being destroyed unnecessarily.

Conviction points set aside are considered unavailable to your character thereafter. They cannot be spent to activate second sight and defenses against the supernatural, to activate edges or to invest into powers. Likewise, Conviction points cannot be *risked* in the creation of a marker; points are already applied to the effort when they're accumulated. Nor can Willpower points be spent to increase an item's effectiveness. That Trait has no bearing beyond your character's mundane, inherent determination.

A marker must be held in hand and make contact with a creature to brand the subject. Firm contact is required; a brush is not sufficient. Striking with the object is effective, assuming the item can withstand the impact. A Judge might even emboss a ring with his symbol and punch targets, leaving a physical indentation *and* an intuitive sign for other imbued to perceive. A successful Dexterity + Brawl roll might be necessary to make contact with an evasive target. No actual damage need be delivered for a mark to take effect.

A marker can affect incorporeal beings as long as your character makes contact with the space they occupy. A spirit possessing a body retains its verdict even after it abandons the host.

A point of Conviction must also be spent when each subject is touched successfully (it's not spent in any failed attempt to mark a creature). The point reinforces your character's belief in the target's relative worth; it's a statement of his faith in his own pronouncement. There is no limit to the total number of verdicts that your character may deliver during his "career," as long as you spend a Conviction point on each of them.

A creature bears your Judge's verdict permanently unless it's altered. Your character can revoke his own sentence, which requires contact again (although no more Conviction need be spent). Another Judge can impose his own verdict on a subject, eliminating your character's judgment completely, as long as his Zeal score is *higher*. A creature can bear only one verdict at a time.

Once a being is marked, your Judge also gains a limited sense of its fate thereafter. He innately knows when his verdict has been violated by another hunter. He gets a sense of dread if a worthy creature is attacked or destroyed by another imbued, or if another hunter is in an unworthy creature's presence and the monster is not harmed or killed. Your Judge automatically knows which of the creatures he has marked is involved, over any distance. He does not know where or how far away the being is.

Verdicts cannot be delivered upon ordinary people. Other hunters are also immune, although an extremist Judge has claimed to label at least one other hunter who defied her will.

A Judge's symbol can be used only by its creator. Attempts to apply it by anyone else, even another arbiter, have no effect. If a marker is thoroughly defaced or damaged or is permanently lost, it loses all of its significance in the hunt. The Conviction invested is lost. Another marker may be created from scratch. Your character may possess only one marker at any one time.

A hunter using second sight notices something strange about a marker, but cannot identify what's odd about it. Perception-enhancing edges such as Discern, Witness or Illuminate offer more information. Perhaps the item is warm to the touch or a hunter code sign not of the creator's design appears. Regardless of what's detected, the object *does not* radiate the menace or inhumanity that monsters do.

Humans perceive nothing special about a marker. A creature with heightened senses might notice something strange about it, but nothing in particular. Neither humans nor monsters detect the label that a Judge imposes upon a subject; only other imbued get a sense of a verdict imposed.

Ultimately, the Storyteller decides when a marker can be created and used effectively. She determines whether your character understands the need to communicate monsters' worth to other imbued. A "hanging judge" might not have much need for a marker if he tends to destroy every creature he encounters. A "soft" judge who dismisses most creatures he encounters might not understand that other hunters are more severe. The Storyteller also decides if the object chosen and the sign it bears are appropriately inherent and unique to your character's identity to become tools of the hunt.

Verdict Versus Brand

Judges' verdict "technique" is different from Defenders' Brand edge. The two are similar in that they label creatures for other imbued to see and understand something about a subject. Brand involves physically harming a subject, however, and the sign imprinted is a hunter code symbol. Judges' verdict inflicts no harm *unto itself* (what harm may be delivered later is another matter). It imposes no physical sign or symbol, either. It communicates a subconscious message to the hunter mind, instead, informing other imbued that a creature has been held in judgment and been found "innocent" or "guilty." How other hunters respond from there is up to them.

It's possible that the two effects draw from some similar sources behind the mission or from the same aspect of Messenger will. Brand seems to be delivered directly from the Heralds, though, whereas the verdict technique appears to originate from Judges' human faculties, resources and skills. This difference may suggest to some that hunters' calling and capabilities in general might not be quite the divine imperative that many interpret them as, but simply a product of human potential.

CHAPTER 6: PRESIDING JUDGES

And let them judge the people at all seasons: and it shall be, that every great matter they shall bring unto thee, but every small matter they shall judge: so shall it be easier for thyself, and they shall bear the burden with thee.
— Exodus 18:22

Becoming a Judge involves being a particular kind of person before the imbuing — having a unique outlook on the world and a particular sense of self. Would-be Judges tend to be planners and thinkers. They don't often spring unprepared into action. They rationalize what the best response is to any situation based on what they know and what they've learned. They're often effective leaders. They seek to get things done carefully and efficiently, organizing and managing their resources, whether it's information, tools or other people. Above all, potential Judges set themselves goals to pursue or purposes to adhere to, and they measure most decisions in regard to how choices fulfill personal agendas or values. Would-be Judges think with the intent to do. They plan with the intent to succeed. And they discriminate with the intent to realize their hopes.

After the imbuing, all of these qualities make these people the facilitators among the imbued. They collect and analyze information about monsters, and they act on instinct when past experience tells them it's the right thing to do. They marshal their fellow imbued who might otherwise strike in vain against the creatures of the night. Finally, awakened arbiters apply their sense of right and wrong to decide the best course on the hunt, and to identify who among monsters and the imbued can be condemned or spared, who is sympathetic and who is anathema.

The following characters represent some of the regular people who have what it takes to set goals in the war and to set enemies apart from friends. They can be the inspiration for or foundation of your own character. Just fill in the blanks to make one of them your own.

HOMEMAKER

I may be out a little late tonight, honey.

Prelude: You're a lucky guy. You had a job once—a series of jobs, in fact. They were okay, but you never really found your *metier*. (That's French for "job you're really good at." One of your kind-of jobs was French tutor.) Everyone who knew you said you were charming, well educated, a gentleman and a scholar. You just never had a great deal of earning potential.

As it happened, you fell in love with a woman who did. Even luckier, she fell in love with you. Her computer-programming job paid enough to cover rent and buy food for both of you, so the money you made restoring antique cars and selling real estate went straight into the home-buying fund. You bought a place in the suburbs when the two of you were just 24. (Okay, your parents helped out. A lot. So did hers.)

You weren't in the house for more than a season before your wife got pregnant. Looking over the books, there was really only one sensible solution. She took as much maternity leave as she could get away with, and after that you were "Mr. Mom."

You loved it. It turned out you were *really* good at being a dad. A born nurturer. You raised a healthy, well-adjusted little girl.

Your daughter's entry into kindergarten left you at loose ends, somewhat. It wasn't so bad at first, but you started thinking about going back to work, or volunteering or finding some way to make yourself useful.

Then came the day you were at the grocery store when one of your neighbors was attacked. The thing appeared to spring from the frozen-food section, but you couldn't get a good look at it. Trying to gave you those strange burns in your eyes that came from staring at snow in bright sunlight. Whatever it was, it held Ms. Madaris by the arm. Was her hand *shattering*? Even stranger, the store-special sign hanging from the ceiling above her read, "ABOMINATION HIDES IN MANY FORMS." What

the hell did that mean, and why did you even notice with all that was happening?

Whatever the sign meant, you could tell that one "form" was wrong. You did what any gentleman-scholar would: You rammed the icy thing with your shopping cart, grabbed Ms. Madaris and got the hell away from there. Everyone else in the store was scattering everywhere, and someone who looked like the manager yelled something about a Freon leak. You could hear sirens in the distance. That's when you noticed that Ms. Madaris' hand wasn't shattered. Her skin looked like the underside of a scab, as if it had just healed.

"Thanks for saving me from that lunatic," she said as she hid her hand under her folded arms.

All you could think was, "*What lunatic?*" And why was she so calm when everyone else was freaking out? She was the one who had been attacked! Without any answers, you mumbled something, scratched your head and grinned your charming grin. But you knew what you'd seen, and you knew Ms. Madaris was hiding something.

Concept: Your various experiences in life have given you a balanced perspective on the world. Everything happens for a reason. One job has always led to a new one, even being a father, so there's some overriding purpose to everything that happens. You understand that some things just have to be done for better things to come along.

Roleplaying Hints: You're ambivalent about the things you've seen and the changes you've experienced. You have an impulse to keep your head down, guard your family and let the rest of the world fend for itself. But so much has gone your way in life that you feel you have to give something back. Maybe this is the job you were always intended for, and everything else was just résumé-building.

Equipment: Dockers slacks, polo shirt, minivan, cell phone

HUNTER-BOOK: JUDGE

NAME: NATURE: Caregiver   PRIMARY VIRTUE: Zeal

PLAYER: DEMEANOR: Conformist   CREED: Judgment

CHRONICLE: CONCEPT: Homemaker   STARTING CONVICTION: 3

ATTRIBUTES

PHYSICAL
Strength — ● ● ○ ○ ○
Dexterity — ● ● ○ ○ ○
Stamina — ● ● ○ ○ ○

SOCIAL
Charisma — ● ● ● ○ ○
Manipulation — ● ● ○ ○ ○
Appearance — ● ● ○ ○ ○

MENTAL
Perception — ● ● ● ○ ○
Intelligence — ● ● ● ○ ○
Wits — ● ● ○ ○ ○

ABILITIES

TALENTS
Alertness — ○ ○ ○ ○ ○
Athletics — ○ ○ ○ ○ ○
Awareness — ○ ○ ○ ○ ○
Brawl — ○ ○ ○ ○ ○
Dodge — ● ○ ○ ○ ○
Empathy — ● ● ○ ○ ○
Expression — ● ● ○ ○ ○
Intimidation — ○ ○ ○ ○ ○
Intuition — ● ○ ○ ○ ○
Leadership — ● ○ ○ ○ ○
Streetwise — ○ ○ ○ ○ ○
Subterfuge — ● ○ ○ ○ ○

SKILLS
Animal Ken — ● ○ ○ ○ ○
Crafts (Car Maintenance) — ● ○ ○ ○ ○
Demolitions — ○ ○ ○ ○ ○
Drive — ● ○ ○ ○ ○
Etiquette — ● ○ ○ ○ ○
Firearms — ○ ○ ○ ○ ○
Melee — ○ ○ ○ ○ ○
Performance — ○ ○ ○ ○ ○
Security — ○ ○ ○ ○ ○
Stealth — ○ ○ ○ ○ ○
Survival — ● ○ ○ ○ ○
Technology — ● ● ○ ○ ○

KNOWLEDGES
Academics — ● ● ○ ○ ○
Bureaucracy — ● ● ○ ○ ○
Computer — ● ● ○ ○ ○
Finance — ● ○ ○ ○ ○
Investigation — ● ○ ○ ○ ○
Law — ● ○ ○ ○ ○
Linguistics (French, Italian) — ● ● ○ ○ ○
Medicine — ○ ○ ○ ○ ○
Occult — ○ ○ ○ ○ ○
Politics — ● ○ ○ ○ ○
Research — ● ● ● ○ ○
Science — ○ ○ ○ ○ ○

ADVANTAGES

BACKGROUNDS
Contacts — ● ● ○ ○ ○
Soulmate (Wife and Daughter) — ● ● ○ ○ ○
Resources — ● ● ○ ○ ○
___ — ○ ○ ○ ○ ○
___ — ○ ○ ○ ○ ○
___ — ○ ○ ○ ○ ○
___ — ○ ○ ○ ○ ○

EDGES

Name	Creed	Level	Trigger
Discern	Judgment	●○○○○	___
Bluster	Redemption	●○○○○	___
___		○○○○○	___
___		○○○○○	___
___		○○○○○	___
___		○○○○○	___

VIRTUES

	MERCY	VISION	ZEAL
1	● X	○	● X
2	○	○	●
3	○	○	○
4	○	○	○
5	○	○	○
6	○	○	○
7	○	○	○
8	○	○	○
9	○	○	○
10	○	○	○

DERANGEMENTS
___
___
___
___
___
___
___

CONVICTION
● ● ● ○ ○ ○ ○ ○ ○ ○

WILLPOWER
● ● ● ● ● ○ ○ ○ ○ ○
☐ ☐ ☐ ☐ ☐ ☐ ☐ ☐ ☐ ☐

EXPERIENCE
[ ]

HEALTH

Bruised		☐
Hurt	-1	☐
Injured	-1	☐
Wounded	-2	☐
Mauled	-2	☐
Crippled	-5	☐
Incapacitated		☐

MINOR FUNCTIONARY

I'm sorry but there seems to be an irregularity with your paperwork.

Prelude: There are over a billion children on planet Earth, and you guess not one of them ever says, "When I grow up, I want to run an emissions test station!" Sure, you're not curing cancer, but the law says cars that pollute have to get fixed or get off the road, so you're a part of the solution. The job has a good pension plan and retirement benefits. You've been there for a decade, so it's practically impossible for you to get canned and the money's okay. It's not fulfilling, but it's not bad.

Most of the time, you actually think about fishing. Damn, you love fishing. You like fishing with your buddies, you like fishing alone, you like fishing in a stream, off a dock, off a boat, in a lake. You even like ice fishing. You got to go deep-sea fishing once, and you liked that, too.

So one day you were on the creek near that abandoned backwoods church, and you got this weird feeling. It was a gorgeous day, but suddenly you felt cold and sick. The crickets were buzzing and made the weirdest sound, just like a voice saying, "THE WORLD IS DEVOURED." You looked up and the churchyard was erupting! Old bones that should have been at rest were getting up! You could see a swarm of shadows that looked like they were fighting over the bones even as the bodies labored to pull themselves up.

Then you heard the howls. Out of the woods came four… things. Animals, but not like any you'd ever seen. They were huge and somehow intelligent-looking. Gnashing and snarling, they charged at the corpses,. It wasn't enough. Every blow from their claws smashed and scattered bones, but for every corpse they tore away from the shadows, there were two more to take its place.

You made your choice. Somehow, you knew which didn't belong, and you found yourself alongside the animals, screaming and smashing bones with the hammer from your tackle box. It still wasn't enough. The best you can describe is that it felt like the shadows were trying to suck out your soul. Then one of the animal-things grabbed you like a rag doll, and the whole pack took off. When you finally stopped, the things seemed to be fighting over you, maybe to decide which one would eat you.

That's when one changed — and looked almost like a person, but still not. It asked some weird questions that you didn't understand. You just shook your head, tried to tell them that if they took you back, you thought maybe this symbol — you could see it in your head — might make things right. Somehow, that calmed most of them down. Even if they didn't take you back to the cemetery, they left you alone and let you live.

You haven't seen anything odd in the woods since then (it's not as if you stopped fishing). But sometimes you do hear howls in the distance. It makes you wonder. The newspaper said there was a tremor in the vicinity of the old church. It also said motorists have vanished in the area. That makes you wonder, too.

What makes you wonder most of all: Sometimes at work, you see things. They look like people, but when you look again, *look closely*, you can see that they aren't. Maybe a hundred people go through your station every day. You don't see a *thing* every day. But since that fishing trip, there hasn't been a week that you haven't seen *something*. Just to feel safer, you spray-painted that symbol in your head onto the roof of your station.

For now, you just jot down their names, addresses and tag numbers. All that information is easy to find — it's right there. You haven't taken any action, though. Not yet.

Concept: You're an invisible minor government functionary who's in a position to see a *lot* of people pass by. No one pays you much attention, and no one expects you to pay attention to them.

Roleplaying Hints: You keep your mouth shut until you have something worthwhile to say. You're extremely patient, unflappable and calm. It's hard to upset you. After all, you've got the government on your side.

Equipment: Clipboard, fishing rod, well maintained pickup truck

HUNTER-BOOK: JUDGE

NAME:

PLAYER:

CHRONICLE:

NATURE: Traditionalist

DEMEANOR: Conformist

CONCEPT: Minor Functionary

PRIMARY VIRTUE: Zeal

CREED: Judgment

STARTING CONVICTION: 3

ATTRIBUTES

PHYSICAL
Strength —— ● ● ● ○ ○
Dexterity —— ● ● ● ○ ○
Stamina (Bear with it) ● ● ● ● ○

SOCIAL
Charisma —— ● ● ○ ○ ○
Manipulation —— ● ● ○ ○ ○
Appearance —— ● ● ○ ○ ○

MENTAL
Perception (Absent Details) ● ● ● ● ○
Intelligence —— ● ● ○ ○ ○
Wits —— ● ● ○ ○ ○

ABILITIES

TALENTS
Alertness —— ● ● ○ ○ ○
Athletics —— ● ● ● ○ ○
Awareness (Natural Disturbances) ● ● ● ● ○
Brawl —— ○ ○ ○ ○ ○
Dodge —— ● ○ ○ ○ ○
Empathy —— ○ ○ ○ ○ ○
Expression —— ○ ○ ○ ○ ○
Intimidation —— ○ ○ ○ ○ ○
Intuition —— ● ● ○ ○ ○
Leadership —— ○ ○ ○ ○ ○
Streetwise —— ○ ○ ○ ○ ○
Subterfuge —— ● ○ ○ ○ ○

SKILLS
Animal Ken —— ● ● ○ ○ ○
Crafts (Car Engines) ● ○ ○ ○ ○
Demolitions —— ○ ○ ○ ○ ○
Drive —— ● ○ ○ ○ ○
Etiquette —— ○ ○ ○ ○ ○
Firearms —— ● ● ○ ○ ○
Melee —— ○ ○ ○ ○ ○
Performance —— ○ ○ ○ ○ ○
Security —— ○ ○ ○ ○ ○
Stealth —— ○ ○ ○ ○ ○
Survival —— ● ● ○ ○ ○
Technology —— ○ ○ ○ ○ ○

KNOWLEDGES
Academics —— ○ ○ ○ ○ ○
Bureaucracy —— ● ● ○ ○ ○
Computer —— ● ● ○ ○ ○
Finance —— ○ ○ ○ ○ ○
Investigation —— ○ ○ ○ ○ ○
Law —— ○ ○ ○ ○ ○
Linguistics —— ○ ○ ○ ○ ○
Medicine —— ○ ○ ○ ○ ○
Occult —— ○ ○ ○ ○ ○
Politics —— ● ● ○ ○ ○
Research —— ○ ○ ○ ○ ○
Science —— ○ ○ ○ ○ ○

ADVANTAGES

BACKGROUNDS
Database —— ● ○ ○ ○ ○
Steel Nerves —— ● ○ ○ ○ ○
Influence —— ● ○ ○ ○ ○
Resources —— ● ● ● ○ ○
—— ○ ○ ○ ○ ○
—— ○ ○ ○ ○ ○
—— ○ ○ ○ ○ ○

EDGES

NAME	CREED	LEVEL	TRIGGER
Discern	Judgment	○○○○○	
Anathema	Judgment	○○○○○	
		○○○○○	
		○○○○○	
		○○○○○	
		○○○○○	

VIRTUES

MERCY	VISION	ZEAL
1 ○ ——	○ ——	● X
2 ○ ——	○ ——	● X
3 ○ ——	○ ——	● X
4 ○ ——	○ ——	○ ——
5 ○ ——	○ ——	○ ——
6 ○ ——	○ ——	○ ——
7 ○ ——	○ ——	○ ——
8 ○ ——	○ ——	○ ——
9 ○ ——	○ ——	○ ——
10 ○ ——	○ ——	○ ——

DERANGEMENTS

_____
_____
_____
_____
_____
_____

CONVICTION
● ● ● ● ○ ○ ○ ○ ○ ○

WILLPOWER
● ● ● ● ○ ○ ○ ○ ○ ○
□ □ □ □ □ □ □ □ □ □

EXPERIENCE
[ ]

HEALTH

Bruised		□
Hurt	-1	□
Injured	-1	□
Wounded	-2	□
Mauled	-2	□
Crippled	-5	□
Incapacitated		□

PROFESSIONAL FRIEND

Are you sure she's legal? She doesn't look legal to me.

Prelude: You've been managing the band since the days when they played biker bars for free beer. You've taken them from sleeping in their van, amid their own discarded hamburger wrappers, to a top-10 single and a tour with a major act. Nowadays, they still sleep in their own filth, but at least they're doing it in four-star hotels and you can get a room of your own.

It hasn't been an easy climb. There have been overdoses, assaults, paternity suits, stalkers, bail-outs, freak-outs and (now and again) dry-outs. But you've stuck with them. They've got talent and charisma and enough sex appeal to earn a platinum record, but deep down you know that the four of them together don't have the common sense God gave one of your short hairs. They're good boys, but they just have a deep, abiding and thorough ignorance of their own best interests.

So even though you're technically their employee, you have to be the authority figure. You have to make sure the groupies are over 21 (you used to stick to 18 until you had to pay a gigantic fine and an equally huge out-of-court settlement after that 19-year-old got alcohol poisoning backstage). You make sure the band is ready to go at something resembling its scheduled time, you keep their drug habits under control, you get them their fair share of the T-shirt profits, and you make sure their sandwiches backstage have the crusts cut off.

And now you have to keep an eye out for *demons*, too. You'd heard there were plenty of predators in the music business, but you always thought it was a metaphor. Then one night there was a riot in the audience, and you saw some 10-foot-tall special effects fighting a gang of corpses. That made the whole crowd hysterical, and your employers too. So you did what any manager would do: Pushed a speaker onto one of the things, dragged the band off stage and yelled, "No refunds!"

Now you've discovered that some club owners you've known for years are dead (and still walking), and most record companies are top-heavy with blood slaves. Is there a sinister supernatural conspiracy controlling world media? If so, can you stop it?

Or could you *use* it to get a number-one hit?

Concept: You manage an up-and-coming rock band. You're used to dealing with big hassles and bad weirdness. But the hassles were never this big before, or this badness this weird.

Roleplaying Hints: No one is exactly your equal. They're either above you (and must be wheedled, cajoled and babied) or they're beneath you (and can be bullied, commanded and condescended to). You're at your best in a crisis. In fact, the past six years with the band have pretty much been one crisis after another.

Equipment: Pager, cell phone, address book, Maalox, embossed leather humidor full of Cuban cigars, gold lighter that you swiped from Mick Jagger (and since convinced him he gave you in a moment of drunken camaraderie).

HUNTER-BOOK JUDGE

NAME: NATURE: Adjudictor   PRIMARY VIRTUE: Zeal
PLAYER: DEMEANOR: Director   CREED: Judgment
CHRONICLE: CONCEPT: Professional Friend   STARTING CONVICTION: 3

ATTRIBUTES

PHYSICAL
Strength ——— ● ● ○ ○ ○
Dexterity ——— ● ● ○ ○ ○
Stamina ——— ● ● ● ○ ○

SOCIAL
Charisma ——— ● ● ● ○ ○
Manipulation (Coercion) ● ● ● ● ○
Appearance ——— ● ● ○ ○ ○

MENTAL
Perception ——— ● ● ● ○ ○
Intelligence ——— ● ● ● ○ ○
Wits ——— ● ● ○ ○ ○

ABILITIES

TALENTS
Alertness ——— ● ○ ○ ○ ○
Athletics ——— ○ ○ ○ ○ ○
Awareness ——— ○ ○ ○ ○ ○
Brawl ——— ○ ○ ○ ○ ○
Dodge ——— ● ○ ○ ○ ○
Empathy ——— ● ● ○ ○ ○
Expression ——— ○ ○ ○ ○ ○
Intimidation ——— ● ○ ○ ○ ○
Intuition ——— ○ ○ ○ ○ ○
Leadership ——— ● ● ○ ○ ○
Streetwise ——— ● ● ○ ○ ○
Subterfuge ——— ● ● ● ○ ○

SKILLS
Animal Ken ——— ○ ○ ○ ○ ○
Crafts ——— ○ ○ ○ ○ ○
Demolitions ——— ○ ○ ○ ○ ○
Drive ——— ● ○ ○ ○ ○
Etiquette ——— ● ○ ○ ○ ○
Firearms ——— ● ○ ○ ○ ○
Melee ——— ○ ○ ○ ○ ○
Performance ——— ○ ○ ○ ○ ○
Security ——— ● ○ ○ ○ ○
Stealth ——— ○ ○ ○ ○ ○
Survival ——— ○ ○ ○ ○ ○
Technology ——— ○ ○ ○ ○ ○

KNOWLEDGES
Academics ——— ● ○ ○ ○ ○
Bureaucracy ——— ● ○ ○ ○ ○
Computer ——— ○ ○ ○ ○ ○
Finance ——— ● ● ○ ○ ○
Investigation ——— ● ○ ○ ○ ○
Law ——— ● ○ ○ ○ ○
Linguistics ——— ○ ○ ○ ○ ○
Medicine ——— ● ○ ○ ○ ○
Occult ——— ○ ○ ○ ○ ○
Politics ——— ○ ○ ○ ○ ○
Research ——— ○ ○ ○ ○ ○
Science ——— ○ ○ ○ ○ ○

ADVANTAGES

BACKGROUNDS
Allies ——— ● ○ ○ ○ ○
Contacts ——— ● ● ● ● ○
Grace Under Pressure ● ● ● ○ ○
Influence ——— ● ● ● ○ ○
Resources ——— ● ● ● ● ○
Steel Nerves ——— ● ● ○ ○ ○
——— ○ ○ ○ ○ ○

EDGES

NAME	CREED	LEVEL	TRIGGER
Discern	Judgment	● ○ ○ ○ ○	———
Ward	Defense	● ○ ○ ○ ○	———
———		○ ○ ○ ○ ○	———
———		○ ○ ○ ○ ○	———
———		○ ○ ○ ○ ○	———
———		○ ○ ○ ○ ○	———

VIRTUES

	MERCY	VISION	ZEAL
1	○	○	● X
2	○	○	● X
3	○	○	●
4	○	○	○
5	○	○	○
6	○	○	○
7	○	○	○
8	○	○	○
9	○	○	○
10	○	○	○

DERANGEMENTS

———
———
———
———
———
———
———

CONVICTION
● ● ● ○ ○ ○ ○ ○ ○ ○

WILLPOWER
● ● ● ● ● ○ ○ ○ ○ ○
□ □ □ □ □ □ □ □ □ □

EXPERIENCE

HEALTH

Bruised		□
Hurt	-1	□
Injured	-1	□
Wounded	-2	□
Mauled	-2	□
Crippled	-5	□
Incapacitated		□

Prominent Judges

The most dedicated, persistent and insightful among Judges have gained some renown among their fellow imbued, either through talk on the street or posts to the Internet. As information-gatherers, organizers, planners and strategists, these people have proved their worth repeatedly by helping less focused and prepared chosen score minor victories — or simply stay alive. And yet, arbiters' reputations begin to tarnish as some become so focused on their personal interpretations of right and wrong, good and evil, that they enforce their ideals upon "lesser" imbued. These Judges become juggernauts, and might not forego their crusade even for "allies."

William Bryant, aka Solomon

Plagued by self-doubt, yet aggressive and decisive in the face of an enemy, William Bryant is a tightly bound bundle of contradictions. He hunts monsters because he believes it's the right thing to do, but he is haunted by guilt that stems from his imbuing. Known as Solomon on hunter mailing lists, William was a successful businessman who transformed the family real-estate brokerage from a perennial also-ran into a force to be reckoned with. William had money, respect and power.

And in a heartbeat, it all turned to ashes.

William's younger brother Roderick was always the family hell-raiser. While William toiled away at the business in the '60s, Roderick lived the life of a bohemian artist. He rarely showed up at family gatherings, and he spent most of his time jetting around the world to attend all the hot gallery openings and art shows.

Years passed as the brothers followed their separate paths. William rarely heard from Roderick and had enough problems of his own that he barely noticed. The brothers' parents insisted on siphoning away a significant portion of the firm's profits for their personal use. William was unconcerned at first, but as competition became heated, he grew increasingly frustrated by the financial handcuffs his parents applied. His relationship with them slowly soured.

After William's parents passed away in the late '80s, he finally learned the truth. The diverted money had actually gone to support Roderick's life as a "starving" artist. Roderick had simply bought his way into the inner circles of the art world, making up for his total lack of talent with money, drugs and an engaging personality. Blaming Roderick for sabotaging his relationship with their parents and for hamstringing the family business, William cut the cash flow and left his brother practically broke and stranded in Europe.

Years passed with not a word between the brothers. Every day, William had to run a business that he knew would be bigger and far more profitable but for his family's abuses. One night, William received a call from Roderick. Little brother was in the States and asked to meet with William. William was imbued during that meeting in his own study. Desperate for support after being cut off, Roderick had fallen in with *things* and had become one himself. Learning of his brother's condition, William flew into a rage, struggled with Roderick and flung him into the fireplace, where the younger brother burned to death.

In the weeks that followed, William learned how pervasive the corruption that had engulfed Roderick really was. There were creatures everywhere, even in the business community. Horrified, William abandoned his former life for one better suited to deal with the truth. Indeed, he led a group of allies for a time before awakening to an even higher calling. Sickened by what he viewed as weakness and cowardice among other imbued, William decided to pass judgment on those not committed to all-out war against the supernatural. By his reckoning, a hunter who is not doing everything in her power to destroy monsters is part of the problem.

Yet, William's conscience gnaws at him; he's not sure whether he killed his brother for being a monster or because he hated Roderick for betraying the family and living a life of luxury he never earned. William is dangerous if only because he feels he has so much to prove to himself. No sacrifice is too great for a man who feels he has already lost everything.

François Loehr, aka Warden

Known on the English hunter lists as "Warden," François Loehr is possibly the most influential of Europe's imbued. His status is partially due to Tarjiman's efforts to translate his well-reasoned and articulate posts from French into English, Arabic and Italian. Even without the widespread dissemination of his ideas, however,

François' connections to law enforcement and to the criminal population of his native Belgium would give him vital information and access in conducting the hunt.

François is the warden of a maximum-security prison in southern Belgium. He was "awakened" during a near-riot, at the same time as two of his guards and three of his prisoners.

François always prided himself on running a fairly clean prison. Sure, there were abuses, there was corruption — but such things happen in the best of penitentiaries, and he felt his was better than most. Now, however, he finds himself tempted to break the rules in the name of higher duty.

His awakened prisoners are ideal pawns in a war against the supernatural. One, a gun smuggler named Poe (see **Hunter Book: Avenger**, p. 94), is a vicious fighter and a remorseless killer. Armande Artaud, a former terrorist, is an arson and demolitions expert serving a life sentence for several firebombings perpetrated in the 1960s. His connections to political radicals are decades stale, but his skill at making buildings burn is as sharp as ever. Finally, there is Klaus Graeber, a burglar and rapist who targeted elderly widows. Graeber reasoned that his victims would be too ashamed to report his crimes to the police. Generally, he was correct. Graeber is nonetheless extremely adept at his chosen craft. He was captured only after being betrayed by his fence as part of a plea bargain.

These three are François' tools, but they cannot be used without cost. Every time he issues them "passes" is an opportunity for escape — an escape that would not only loose a menace from prison, but that would cost him his position and draw the attention of higher authorities and his prey to himself… and his family.

It's not easy for François to sneak the prisoners out. They can be shuffled into the infirmary and extricated from there. They can be assigned to solitary confinement as an excuse for absences from the general population. Armande is even eligible for work release, under highly controlled circumstances. But François knows that every time he arranges a mission, he necessarily shows his prisoners the weaknesses in his facility. Yet he cannot bring himself to look away while blood drinkers infest NATO and sorcerers exert their influence in the European Community.

As he becomes more familiar with the community of awakened in Europe, François hopes to make use of his three weapons less frequently. Yet, part of him hates risking the lives of decent folk against monsters — not only because Poe, Klaus and Armande won't be missed if they're killed, but because the three prisoners are more likely to succeed and survive.

Profile

Attributes: Strength 3, Dexterity 2, Stamina 3, Charisma 3, Manipulation 2, Appearance 2, Perception 3, Intelligence 2, Wits 3

Abilities: Academics 1, Alertness 2, Brawl 3, Bureaucracy 3, Computer 1, Dodge 3, Drive 1, Etiquette 2, Firearms 2, Intimidation 3, Investigation 3, Law 2, Leadership 3, Linguistics 2, Security 3, Streetwise 2, Subterfuge 2

Backgrounds: Allies 2, Arsenal 1, Contacts 3, Influence 3, Resources 3

Edges: (Judgment) Discern, Burden; (Defense) Ward

Zeal: 5, **Conviction**: 5, **Willpower**: 5

Dr. Carleton Van Wyk, aka Doctor 119

Carleton Van Wyk was never a very good physician. His skills were adequate, but his brusque and

clinical manner did not endear him to his patients. He eventually moved into medical research and forensics. He did much better operating on people who couldn't complain — until one corpse sat up and tried to claw his face off.

Carleton survived, but was unable to explain the condition of the morgue to the hospital. He was censured by the AMA for "unethical research" and kept his license only by cashing in some major favors.

Once fired by the hospital, he became a discreet abortionist by profession, but spent the majority of his time striving to learn the demonstrable, provable, scientific truth about the walking dead. He doesn't think of it as a way to clear his name (not consciously, anyway). He genuinely wants to help humanity. He just doesn't deal well with individual humans.

It doesn't help that many of the people he's met since his imbuing have wound up dead. Jared Shoemaker and Scott Fairlane in Chicago, three others in Cleveland — all deceased, while he survives. The worst by far was Duane Kinniard in Cincinnati. Carleton and Duane worked as "deprogrammers" for the Blood Cult Awareness Network, seizing and trying to rescue those who were ensnared by "blood cults." Only Carleton and Duane were aware of the true foundation of these groups, and Duane wound up corrupted and co-opted by the forces they fought… until Carleton killed him.

Carleton is scrupulously polite, but generally seems standoffish, superior and a bit of a "cold fish." He tries very hard to keep his emotions under control, but every now and then they burst forth in displays of anger, sorrow or hysteria. Carleton is always profoundly embarrassed after he loses his composure.

Currently, he plans to return to Chicago, in hopes that the heat has died down there.

Profile

Attributes: Strength 2, Dexterity 3, Stamina 2, Charisma 1, Manipulation 2, Appearance 3, Perception (Small Details) 5, Intelligence (Logical Analysis) 4, Wits 3

Abilities: Academics 1, Alertness (Normal Sight) 5, Brawl 1, Bureaucracy 1, Computer 1, Dodge 3, Drive 1, Etiquette 3, Firearms 3, Investigation 3, Linguistics 1, Medicine 3, Research 2, Science 3

Backgrounds: Allies 3, Grace Under Pressure 5, Resources 3, Steel Nerves 3

Edges: (Judgment) Discern, Burden; (Defense) Ward, Rejuvenate; (Visionary) Foresee

Zeal: 6, **Vision:** 2, **Conviction:** 7, **Willpower:** 9

Erick Franco, aka Shophet

Duty was always foremost for Erick Franco even before his imbuing. In his California youth, he felt it was his duty to be a good Jew. During his stint in the Israeli army, he knew he had to protect the Jewish homeland. So, years later, despite having drifted away from his faith and having ended his time as a soldier, when he heard the Call and saw the dead things he knew it was duty time again.

Erick believed that he and the others imbued alongside him had been given a new form of a very old duty, that all of them were *shophetim*, the judges who guided the ancient Israelites in times of war and oppression. But Erick and his allies had a greater charge than the *shophetim* of old: They had to guide all humanity in an invisible war against dybbuks and worse.

Soon enough, Erick realized that not all imbued were created equal. He ran afoul of two hunters, Peleus and Van Owen, whose depredations easily were as evil as anything the hidden creatures did. Erick killed Van Owen and intended the same for Peleus when the latter seemingly died trying to kill one of Erick's imbued allies.

Erick's dismay after learning of Peleus' survival (*return?*) grew into an obsession with the other hunter's destruction. Along with two imbued associates, Erick became a wanderer searching for his nemesis and combating nightcrawlers. Unfortunately, he recently gained a powerful new enemy and lost his longtime allies Sarin and Michelle. Now, he is pursuer and pursued, ever a step behind Peleus and just ahead of a sorcerer named Koepell°.